# THE PSYCHOLOGY
## OF SCIENCE

THE JOHN DEWEY SOCIETY LECTURESHIP — NUMBER EIGHT

# THE PSYCHOLOGY
# OF SCIENCE

*A Reconnaissance*

by

## ABRAHAM H. MASLOW

PROFESSOR OF PSYCHOLOGY
BRANDEIS UNIVERSITY

FOREWORD BY

### Arthur G. Wirth

CHAIRMAN, THE JOHN DEWEY SOCIETY
COMMISSION ON LECTURES

HARPER & ROW, PUBLISHERS, NEW YORK AND LONDON

501.9
M397p

# Contents

Foreword, by Arthur G. Wirth                                           ix

Preface                                                               xiii

Acknowledgments                                                       xix

1. Mechanistic and Humanistic Science                                  1

2. Acquiring Knowledge of a Person as a Task
   for the Scientist                                                   7

3. The Cognitive Needs Under Conditions of Fear
   and of Courage                                                     20

4. Safety Science and Growth Science: Science as
   a Defense                                                          33

5. Prediction and Control of Persons?                                 40

6. Experiential Knowledge and Spectator Knowl-
   edge                                                               45

7. Abstracting and Theorizing                                         66

8. Comprehensive Science and Simpleward Science                       72

9. Suchness Meaning and Abstractness Meaning                          84

10. Taoistic Science and Controlling Science                          95

11. Interpersonal (I-Thou) Knowledge as a
    Paradigm for Science                                             102

12. Value-Free Science                                               119

13. Stages, Levels, and Degrees of Knowledge                         128

14. The Desacralization and the Resacralization
    of Science                                                       138

Bibliography                                                         153

Index                                                                159

49723

for Bertha

# Foreword

by

ARTHUR G. WIRTH,

CHAIRMAN, COMMISSION ON LECTURES,

The John Dewey Society for the Study of Education and Culture

Professor Maslow presents us with a book in the honorable tradition of dissent. In doing so he challenges the dominant *Weltanschauung* that governs the definition of problems and methodologies in the sciences concerned with human personality and behavior. He charges, for example, that the mainstream methodology in psychological research, modeled after the mechanomorphic tradition of the physical sciences, veils us from a fuller knowledge of human personality—a knowledge which we sorely need. Because the research techniques of the mechanistic tradition serve so well in the study of animal behavior, and some aspects of human behavior, its practitioners have come to argue that these methods constitute the sole avenue to scientific knowledge about personality. Professor Maslow believes that such adherents are guilty of attempting to define the whole phenomenon of the human being in terms of the parts they can manipulate well. He asks behavioral scientists to confront the possibility that personal security needs may be a factor in the singleminded insistence on the authority of orthodox methodology.

A case in point is the training program for researchers. He

argues that training based solely on the mechanistic model tends to sponsor safe investigations, limited to inquiries that may be managed easily by the methodology. This has the effect of ruling out significant but more intractable questions that deal with the whole person—with subjective or self-knowledge, with deeper knowledge of "a single person," and with the higher human qualities such as altruism and integrity. (We may ask, too, if a selective factor operates to retain only students content to stay within the fold.) If our knowledge of human personality is to advance we need researchers with the courage and imagination to confront the "hot" questions that typically get postponed until "later."

He notes that an ethnocentric attachment to the scientific *Weltanschauung* of the West can bar us from ideas from other intellectual frameworks that may advance our knowledge about dimensions of human experience. He is bold to offer "Taoistic science" as one such possibility.

Why should a man hurl his lance against the citadel and risk the rocks and hot oil he may expect in return? Professor Maslow's discontent derives from his personal experience as a psychologist. He was schooled in the experimental tradition of John Watson and was competent in its practice. But he felt the lure of questions that did not fit the rationale of that laboratory. As a clinical psychologist and therapist he became interested in understanding the conditions that made for productive, mature persons—or with factors that led to crippling. As a knowledge seeker he examined the concepts and tools available from his behaviorist training and found them of little use or relevance for the question he wanted to investigate. To remain within the ongoing methodology would have forced him either to relinquish the problems about which he was curious or to give spurious definitions to his subject matter. "If the only tool you have is a hammer, it is tempting to treat everything as if it were a nail." He was not interested in nails, and he refused to hang that label on the nonnail world he wished to understand. If he had surrendered to the temptation, we would not have this book before us.

As fair-minded readers will recognize, Dr. Maslow's intent is not to debunk, nor is it to pretend to present a "new" science for an old and discredited one. His plea is for attitudes that would support imaginary ventures (subject to the canons of criticism) that would enable scientific investigations to move beyond the established trenchworks into relatively unexplored terrain. This calls for new strategies. But he makes clear that the concepts he suggests are inclusive of mechanistic science rather than alternatives to it. Since the point is vitally important, his own words may be repeated: "I believe mechanistic science (which in psychology takes the form of behaviorism) to be not incorrect but rather too narrow and limited to serve as a *general* philosophy."

Dr. Maslow's dissatisfaction with the limitations of current research techniques forced him to reappraise the enterprise of science itself. He came to conclude that the first obligation of science is to confront all of reality as man experiences it—to describe, to understand, to "accept" all that is. A cardinal sin of the scientist is to deny reality, or to refuse to confront aspects of it because they are not amenable to the best-honed tools at hand.

He accepts and respects the other obligations of science: to be objective and to seek comprehensive, abstract, and lawful ordering. He knows that sheer immersion in experience may lead to dilettantism or quackery. He warns, however, that the love for abstract system-making contains its own dangers. If we mistake the abstractions or the systems with reality itself, we delude ourselves. And if we treat human beings merely as objects to be controlled instead of persons to be released for growth, we may become partners to dehumanization. He returns to an insistence that students of Dewey will recognize as a recurrent theme of that thinker: reliable insights into the world require a never-ending interplay of theoretical abstraction and the stuff of experience. We settle needlessly for partial knowledge when we opt for one without the check of the other.

To sharpen the issues Professor Maslow frames and pursues questions like the following: How adequate are the concepts and methods of classical science for acquiring knowledge about the human person? What are the consequences of the inadequacies? What counterproposals can be offered and tested? What are the implications for those who plan programs to train researchers?

Enough has been said to lead the reader to Professor Maslow's own exposition. It is clear that this short book cannot be the last word on the subject. It is equally clear that it brings up value questions that are as vital as any for those who would make human beings the subject of scientific inquiry.

The annual John Dewey Lecture is delivered each February at a joint meeting of the John Dewey Society for the Study of Education and Culture and the National Society for College Teachers of Education. This book is an elaboration of a paper read by Professor Maslow on that occasion. The intention of the lecture program is to provide a setting where able thinkers from various sectors of our intellectual life can direct their most searching thought to problems that involve the relation of education to culture. The John Dewey Society is confident that the kind of challenge presented by Professor Maslow makes his contribution a noteworthy contribution to this series.

# Preface

This book concentrates on science as a product of the human nature of the scientist, not only of the cautious, conventional scientist but also of the daring, breakthrough revolutionary. To some extent this overlaps with the kind of science generated by the psychologically healthy scientist. This essay may be considered to be a continuation of my *Motivation and Personality* and especially of the first three chapters in which the psychology of science and of the scientist are dealt with specifically.

One basic thesis which emerges from this approach is that the model of science in general, inherited from the impersonal sciences of things, objects, animals, and part-processes, is limited and inadequate when we attempt to know and to understand whole and individual persons and cultures. It was primarily the physicists and the astronomers who created the *Weltanschauung* and the subculture known as Science (including all its goals, methods, axiomatic values, concepts, languages, folkways, prejudices, selective blindnesses, hidden assumptions). This has been pointed out by so many as to amount to a truism by now. But only recently has it been demonstrated just how and where this impersonal model failed with the personal, the unique, the holistic. Nor has an alternative model yet been offered to deal validly with the fully human person.

This I attempt to do in this book. I hope to show that these limitations of classical science are not intrinsically necessary. In the broad sense, science can be defined as powerful and inclusive enough to reclaim many of the cognitive problems from which it has had to abdicate because of its hidden but fatal weakness—its inability to deal impersonally with the personal, with the problems of value, of individuality, of consciousness, of beauty, of transcendence, of ethics. In principle, at least, science should be capable of generating normative psychologies of psychotherapy, of personal development, of eupsychian or utopian social psychology, of religion, of work, play, and leisure, of esthetics, of economics, and politics, and who knows what else?

I conceive such a change in the nature of science to be one delayed fulfillment of the revolutionary potential of the psychoanalytic movement. This fulfillment was delayed ironically by the fact that Freud was raised in the nineteenth-century version of science along with its determinism, causality, atomism, and reductiveness. Even though he spent his whole life unwittingly cutting the ground out from under this version of science and, in fact, destroying it, along with all pure rationalisms, Freud remained loyal to its *Weltanschauung* so far as I can tell. Unfortunately, none of the other great contributors to the development of modern psychodynamics—Adler, Jung, Reich, Rank, Horney, Fromm—were scientists and so did not address themselves directly to this problem. The only psychoanalyst I can think of now who has taken this job seriously is Lawrence Kubie. I hope very much that other psychoanalysts and psychodynamicists will continue to criticize science from the point of view of their data. I remember bursting out in irritation at one meeting. "Why do you keep asking if psychoanalysis is scientific enough? Why don't you ask if science is psychodynamic enough?" I ask the same question here.

This process of rehumanizing (and trans-humanizing) science can help to strengthen the nonpersonal sciences as well. Something like this is happening in various fields of biology, especially in experimental embryology. Out of the intrinsic dynamics of the facts themselves, this discipline has had to become holistic. See for instance the powerful writings of Ludwig von Bertalanffy. The hybrid "field" of psychosomatic medicine is also generating a profound critique of traditional science. So is endocrinology. Ultimately, I believe, all of biology will have to shake itself loose from a pure physical-chemical reductiveness, or at least it will have to transcend it in an inclusive way, that is, in a hierarchical integration.

My restlessness with classical science became serious only when I started asking new questions about the higher reaches of human nature. Only then did the classical scientific model in which I had been trained fail me. It was then that I had to invent, *ad hoc,* new methods, new concepts, and new words in order to handle my data well. Before this, for me, Science had been One, and there was but One Science. But now it looked as if there were *two* Sciences for me, one for my new problems, and one for everything else. But more recently, perhaps ten or fifteen years ago, it began to appear that these two Sciences could be generalized into One Science again. This *new* Science looks different however; it promises to be more inclusive and more powerful than the old One Science.

I have been disturbed not only by the more "anal" scientists and the dangers of their denial of human values in science, along with the consequent amoral technologizing of all science. Just as dangerous are some of the critics of orthodox science who find it too skeptical, too cool and nonhuman, and then reject it altogether as a danger to human values. They become "antiscientific" and even anti-intellectual. This is a real danger among some psychotherapists and clinical psychologists, among artists, among some seriously religious people, among some of the people who are interested in Zen, in Taoism, in existentialism, "experientialism," and the like. Their alternative to science is often sheer freakishness and cultishness, uncritical and selfish exaltation of mere personal experiencing, over-reliance on impulsivity (which they confuse with spontaneity), arbitrary whimsicality and emotionality, unskeptical enthusiasm, and finally navel-watching and solipsism. This is a real danger. In the political realm, antiscience could wipe out mankind just as easily as could value-free, amoral, technologized science. We should remember the Nazis and Fascists with their call to blood and to sheer instinct, and their hostility to freely-probing intellect and to cool rationality.

I certainly wish to be understood as trying to *enlarge* science, not destroy it. It is not necessary to choose between experiencing and abstracting. Our task is to integrate them.

The discursive style used in this book follows the lecture form. Lecturing permits the speaker to be more personal, to use examples from his own experience, to express his own opinions, doubts, and conjectures. I have taken advantage of these possibilities. And for this same reason, I have not made any systematic effort to document my theses with detailed references to the scientific literature. Nor does this book attempt to "cover the subject," or to be scholarly in a comprehensive or systematic way.

This book is a condensation of the systematic and comprehensive volume that I had hoped to write but couldn't. Partly this was due to the limitation of space and the pressure of time imposed by the lecture format. But it was also due to discovering Michael Polanyi's great book, *Personal Knowledge,* just as I had worked up a systematic outline and started writing.

This profound work, which is certainly required reading for our generation, does much of what I had planned to do, and solves many of the problems which had concerned me. I changed my plans to focus particularly on some of the explicitly psychological problems and omitted or treated only briefly several of the topics I had planned to cover.

# Acknowledgments

I should like to refer the reader to the prefaces to my previous books in which I expressed many of my intellectual obligations. In addition to those acknowledgments, I should like to add the following.

I made a most unusual experiment with my good friend and collaborator, Dr. Harry Rand, a psychoanalyst. He and I had been discussing through the years the psychodynamics of the intellectual and scientific life, of learning and teaching, and of their pathology. At one time or another, we talked about many of the topics touched on in this book, and I must owe far more to these discussions than I could be aware of. But more specifically, about a year ago, while preparing this manuscript, I fell simultaneously into a long spell of insomnia and into a writing block, something I had never experienced before. Although friendship has long been considered a bar to psychoanalytic work, we decided to try it. I am glad to report a most successful outcome after about thirty hours or so of "intellectual psychoanalysis" or whatever it ought to be called. We recommend that others try this most interesting experiment so that experience may accumulate and perhaps lead one day to more "normal" and generalized research. For this help, I owe a great debt of gratitude to Dr. Rand.

Within the field of what I have called the psychology of science, overlapping often with the philosophy of science, I must refer to the bibliography of this book as a list of acknowledgments of intellectual indebtedness. Even this is far from complete. Within it, however, there are still more special obligations which I should like to acknowledge in addition to my very special one to Polanyi.

I stumbled across the writings of David Lindsay Watson by sheer accident years ago and was much influenced by his iconoclasm. Like many forerunners, he has not been sufficiently appreciated, honored, or even noticed. Any one interested in my book will certainly be interested in Watson's. I strongly urge that his works be read.

I learned much from the pioneering researches of Anne Roe as well as from her most recent follow-ups. I regret that I was not able to include a chapter on her work and on later studies of this type.

The writings of Jacob Bronowski were especially formative and influential. Frank Manuel's studies of Isaac Newton and our discussions of them taught me a great deal. The impact of these discussions is most evident in some portions of my last chapter, especially the section on good-humored skepticism. Northrop's *The Meeting of East and West* was important in developing my thinking. So also was Kuhn's monograph *The Structure of Scientific Revolutions*. I have profited much from discussions with Aldous Huxley as well as from his writings.

I had so many references to and so many quotations from *Manas* that I finally deleted them in favor of this blanket acknowledgment of my heavy indebtedness to this most distinguished of the humanistic journals.

Finally I wish to express my thanks to Mrs. Alice Duffy for her very professional job of typing and retyping this manuscript.

ABRAHAM H. MASLOW

Brandeis University
Waltham, Massachusetts
February 1966

# THE PSYCHOLOGY
## OF SCIENCE

# 1

# Mechanistic and Humanistic Science

This book is not an argument *within* orthodox science; it is a critique (à la Gödel) *of* orthodox science and of the ground on which it rests, of its unproved articles of faith, and of its taken-for-granted definitions, axioms, and concepts. It is an examination of science as one philosophy of knowledge among other philosophies. It rejects the traditional but unexamined conviction that orthodox science is *the* path to knowledge or even that it is the only reliable path. I consider this conventional view to be philosophically, historically, psychologically and sociologically naïve. As a philosophical doctrine orthodox science is ethnocentric, being Western rather than universal. It is unaware that it is a product of time and place, that it is not an eternal, unchangeable, inexorably progressing truth. Not only is it relative to time, place, and local culture, but it is also characterologically relative, for I believe it to be a reflection far more narrowly of the cautious, obsessional world view centered on the need for safety than of a more mature, generally human, comprehensive view of life. Such weaknesses as these become especially glaring in the area of psychology, where the goal is the knowledge of persons and of their actions and works.

In spite of the fact that many great scientists have escaped these mistakes, and in spite of the fact that they have written much to support their larger view of science as nearly synonymous with all knowledge rather than merely as knowledge respectably attained, they have not prevailed. As T. S. Kuhn (30)[1] has shown, the style of "normal science" has been established not by the great eagles of science—the paradigm-makers, the discoverers, the revolutionizers—but on the contrary by the majority of "normal scientists," who are rather like those tiny marine animals building up a common coral reef. And so it is that science has come to mean primarily patience, caution, care, slowness, the art of not making mistakes, rather than courage, daring, taking big chances, gambling everything on a single throw, and "going for broke." Or to say this another way: our orthodox conception of science as mechanistic and ahuman seems to me one local part-manifestation or expression of the larger, more inclusive world view of mechanization and dehumanization. (An excellent exposition of this development can be found in the first three chapters of Floyd Matson's *Broken Image*.)

But in this century, and especially in the last decade or two, a counter philosophy has been rapidly developing along with a considerable revolt against the mechanistic, dehumanized view of man and the world. It might be called a rediscovery of man and his human capacities, needs, and aspirations. These humanly based values are being restored to politics, to industry, to religion, and also to the psychological and social sciences. I might put it so: while it was necessary and helpful to dehumanize planets, rocks, and animals, we are realizing more and more strongly that it is *not* necessary to dehumanize the human being and to deny him human purposes.

Yet a certain rehumanization is also taking place even in the nonhuman and impersonal sciences, as Matson points out.

---

[1] Italic numbers refer to the corresponding works listed in the Bibliography; where applicable, page numbers in Roman type follow the bibliographic reference. For example: "*18*, 41, 45" would mean pages 41 and 45 in the eighteenth book listed in the Bibliography.

This change is part of a larger and more inclusive, more "humanistic" world view. For the time being these two great philosophic orientations, the mechanistic and the humanistic, exist simultaneously like some species-wide two-party system.[2]

I consider that my effort to rehumanize science and knowledge for myself (but most particularly the field of psychology) is part of this larger social and intellectual development. It is definitely in accord with the *Zeitgeist,* as Bertalanffy pointed out in 1949 (*7,* 202):

> The evolution of science is not a movement in an intellectual vacuum; rather it is both an expression and a driving force of the historical process. We have seen how the mechanistic view projected (itself) through all fields of cultural activity. Its basic conceptions of strict causality, of the summative and random character of natural events, of the aloofness of the ultimate elements of reality, governed not only physical theory but also the analytic, summative, and machine-theoretical viewpoints of biology, the atomism of classical psychology, and the sociological *bellum omnium contra omnes.* The acceptance of living beings as machines, the domination of the modern world by technology, and the mechanization of mankind are but the extension and practical application of the mechanistic conception of physics. The recent evolution in science signifies a general change in the intellectual structure which may well be set beside the great revolutions in human thought.

Or if I may quote myself (1943) saying this in another way (*38,* 23):

> . . . The search for a fundamental datum (in psychology) is itself a reflection of a whole world view, a scientific philosophy which assumes an atomistic world—a world in which complex things are built up out of simple elements. The first task of such a

---

[2] I do not mean to imply that "rehumanization" as a world view is necessarily the last word. Even before rehumanization has been well established, the shape of a world view beyond it is already beginning to be discernible. I shall speak below of selfless person-transcending values and realities, i.e., of a higher level of humanness, self-actualization, authenticity, and identity, in which the person becomes part of the world rather than its center.

scientist then is to reduce the so-called complex to the so-called simple. This is to be done by analysis, by finer and finer separating until we come to the irreducible. This task has succeeded well enough elsewhere in science, for a time at least. In psychology it has not.

This conclusion exposes the essentially theoretical nature of the entire reductive effort. It must be understood that this effort is *not* of the essential nature of science in general. It is simply a reflection or implication in science of an atomistic, mechanical world view that we now have good reason to doubt. Attacking such reductive efforts is then not an attack on science in general, but rather on one of the possible attitudes towards science.

And further on in the same paper (p. 60):

This artificial habit of abstraction, or working with reductive elements, has worked so well and has become so ingrained a habit that the abstractors and reducers are apt to be amazed at anyone who denies the empirical or phenomenal validity of these habits. By smooth stages they convince themselves that this is the way in which the world is actually constructed, and they find it easy to forget that even though it is useful it is still artificial, conventionalized, hypothetical—in a word, that it is a man-made system that is imposed upon an interconnected world in flux. These peculiar hypotheses about the world have the right to fly in the face of common sense but only for the sake of demonstrated convenience. When they are no longer convenient, or when they become hindrances, they must be dropped. It is dangerous to see in the world what we have put into it rather than what is actually there. Let us say this flatly—that atomistic mathematics or logic is, in a certain sense, a theory about the world, and any description of it in terms of this theory the psychologist may reject as unsuited to his purposes. It is clearly necessary for methodological thinkers to proceed to the creation of logical and mathematical systems that are more closely in accord with the nature of the world of modern science.

It is my impression that the weaknesses of classical science show up most obviously in the fields of psychology and ethnology. Indeed, when one wishes knowledge of persons or of societies, mechanistic science breaks down altogether. At any rate, this book is primarily an effort within psychology to enlarge the conception of science so as to make it more capable of dealing with persons, especially fully developed and fully human persons.

I conceive this to be not a divisive effort to oppose one "wrong" view with another "right" view, nor to cast out anything. The conception of science in general and of psychology in general, of which this book is a sample, is *inclusive* of mechanistic science. I believe mechanistic science (which in psychology takes the form of behaviorism) to be not incorrect but rather too narrow and limited to serve as a *general* or comprehensive philosophy.[3]

[3] "In his law of the growth of the great kingdoms Newton was performing for political history a function similar, *mutatis mutandis,* to his discovery of the laws of motion (it was universal and it was simple), though he considered that prophets like Daniel had anticipated him by depicting the same history of the 'four kingdoms' in hieroglyphic language. Newton never wrote a history of men—they do not seem to count as individuals in his narrative—but of bodies politic as he had written a history of bodies physical. These agglomerations did not spring into being suddenly; like the physical planets they too had an 'original,' a history of creation, an extension in space which could be marked chronologically, and they too would have an end. Newton's chronological writings might be called the mathematical principles of the consolidation of empires because they dealt primarily with quantities of geographic space in a temporal sequence; the individuals mentioned in his histories, usually royal personages, were merely signposts marking the progressive expansion of territories; they have no distinctive human qualities. The subject matter of his history was the action of organized political land masses upon one another; crucial events were the fusion of previously isolated smaller units or the destruction of cohesive kingdoms by quantitatively superior forces. Moreover, Newton's principles of the consolidation of empires were equally true throughout the geographic world, in China as well as in Egypt.

"When men did at times obtrude into his histories, Newton almost unconsciously imputed simple motives to their actions. His kings are automatonlike agents in the acquisition of power and the extension of dominion. When on rare occasions he examines them more closely they invariably operate in terms of the seventeenth-century balance of power principles. If an empire is in a state of distraction alliances are made by its enemies to take quick advantage of its weakness. Royal lust for acquisition is based on 'vanity' and other such staples of contemporary literary psychology. All dynasts, ancient and modern, look alike; they merely have different titles, and the theaters where they perform have different place names. They have no more character, either psychological or historical, than persons described in Apollodorus' *Library*. Newton found no proofs of the glory of God, as John Ray had, in the complexities and beauties of the organic world; he sought His impress almost exclusively in laws of the physical-astronomical universe. It was not the passions of men in history but the principles of the physical-astronomical universe. It was not the wondrous combination of parts in the eye but the principles of optics which stirred his imagination. It was not the passions of men in history but the principles of the physical growth of monarchies and the chronology of kingdoms that moved him. Everything human is alien to him—at least insofar as he expressed himself on mankind. His history hardly ever records a feeling, an emotion. Nations are for the most part puppets, neutral as astronomical bodies; they invade and they are in their turn conquered; they grow larger and kingdoms coalesce—nothing more until Rome arises to rule the world." F. Manuel, *Isaac Newton, Historian* (Harvard Univ. Pr., 1963), pp. 137–138.

# 2

# Acquiring Knowledge of a Person as a Task for the Scientist

What alterations in attitude toward science are called for by this change in world view? Where did these changes come from? What forced them upon our attention? Why is the mechanistic, nonhuman model giving way to a human-centered paradigm?

In my own history this clash in scientific world view first took the form of living simultaneously with two psychologies that had little to do with each other. In my career as an experimentalist in the laboratory, I felt quite comfortable and capable with my heritage of scientific orthodoxy. (See complete bibliography in *51*). Indeed it was John B. Watson's optimistic credo (in *Psychologies of 1925*) that had brought me and many others into the field of psychology. His programmatic writings promised a clear road ahead. I felt—with great exhilaration—that it guaranteed progress. There could be a *real* science of psychology, something solid and reliable to depend on to advance steadily and irreversibly from one certainty to the next. It offered a technique (conditioning) which gave promise of solving all problems and a wonderfully convincing philosophy (positivism, objectivism) that was easy to understand and to apply, that protected us against all the mistakes of the past.

But insofar as I was a psychotherapist, an analysand, a

father, a teacher, and a student of personality—that is, insofar as I dealt with whole persons—"scientific psychology" gradually proved itself to be of little use. In this realm of persons I found far greater sustenance in "psychodynamics," especially the psychologies of Freud and Adler, psychologies that were clearly not "scientific" by the definitions of the day.

It was as if psychologists then lived by two mutually exclusive sets of rules, or as if they spoke two different languages for different purposes. If they were interested in working with animals, or with part-processes in human beings, they could be "experimental and scientific psychologists." But if they were interested in whole persons, these laws and methods were not of much help.

I think that we can understand these philosophical changes best if we contrast their relative effectiveness in handling these scientifically new human and personal problems. Let us ask the questions: suppose I wish to know more about the nature of the human person—about you, for instance, or about some other particular person—what is the most promising and most fruitful way to go about it? How useful are the assumptions and methods and conceptualizations of classical science? Which approach is best? Which techniques? Which epistemology? Which style of communication? Which tests and which measurements? Which a priori assumptions about the nature of knowledge? What do we mean by the word "know"?

### NOMOTHETIC AND IDIOGRAPHIC KNOWING

First of all, we should be aware that this question itself about *a* person, is ruled out by many scientists as trivial or "unscientific." Practically all scientists (of the impersonal) proceed on the tacit or explicit assumption that one studies classes or groups of things, not single things. Of course you actually look at one thing at a time, one paramecium, one piece of quartz, one particular kidney, one schizophrenic. But each one is treated as a sample of a species or of a class, and therefore as interchangeable. (See *31* on Galilean and Aristotelian science.) No ordinary scientific journal would accept a meticulous description of a particular white rat or a particular fish. The main business of classical science is generalization, abstracting what is common to all white rats or fish, etc. (Teratology, the study of exceptions and of "marvels," i.e., of monsters, is of no great scientific interest except as it teaches more about the "normal" processes of embryology by contrast.)

Any one sample is just that, a sample; it is not itself. It stands for something. It is anonymous, expendable, not unique, not sacred, not *sine qua non;* it has no proper name all its own and is not worthwhile in itself as a particular instance. It is interesting only insofar as it represents something other than itself. This is what I mean when I say that orthodox, textbook science normally and centrally studies classes of things, or interchangeable objects. There are no individuals in a textbook of physics or chemistry, let alone mathematics.

Taking this as a centering point, as typical and as paradigmatic, astronomers, geologists, and biologists, dealing as they sometimes do with unique instances such as a particular planet or a particular earthquake or a particular sweetpea or drosophila, yet move toward generality as the approved way of becoming more scientific. For most scientists this is the only direction in which scientific knowledge grows.

And yet as we move further away from the central model of impersonal, generalizing, similarity-seeking science, we find that there *are* people who are systematically and persistently curious about unique, idiographic, individual instances that are not interchangeable, that are *sui generis* and happen only once—some psychologists, for instance, and some ethnologists, some biologists, some historians, and of course all human beings in their intimate personal relations. (I am sure physicists and chemists have spent as much time puzzling over their wives as they have over atoms.)

My original question was: if I want to know a person, what is the best way to go about doing it? And now I can rephrase this question more pointedly. How good for this purpose are the usual procedures of normal physical science (which, remember, is the widely accepted paradigm for *all* the sciences and even for all knowledge of any kind)? In general my answer is that they are not very good at all. As a matter of fact, they are practically useless if I want not only to know about you but also to understand you. If I want to know a person in those aspects of personhood that are most important to me, I have learned that I must go about this task in a different way, use different techniques and operate upon profoundly different philosophical assumptions about the nature of detachment, objectivity, subjectivity, reliability of knowledge, value, and precision. I shall try to spell out some of these below.

First of all I must approach a person as an individual unique and peculiar, the sole member of his class. Of course it is true that the normal scientific, abstract, psychological knowledge that I have accumulated through the years helps me to place him at least crudely in the classification of the whole human species. I know what to look for. I can make a rough characterological, constitutional, psychiatric, persono-logical, and intellectual rating (IQ) far better than I could twenty-five years ago. And yet it is also true that all this nomothetic knowledge (of law, of generalization, of aver-ages) is useful only if it can channel through and improve my idiographic knowledge (of this particular individual). Any clinician knows that in getting to know another person it is best to keep your brain out of the way, to look and listen totally, to be completely absorbed, receptive, passive, patient, and waiting rather than eager, quick, and impatient. It does not help to start measuring, questioning, calculating, or testing out theories, categorizing, or classifying. If your brain is too busy, you won't hear or see well. Freud's term "free-floating attention" describes well this noninterfering, global, receptive, waiting kind of cognizing another person.

To the seeker for knowledge about persons, abstract knowledge, scientific laws and generalizations, statistical tables and expectations are all useful if they can be humanized, personalized, individualized, focused into this particular interpersonal relationship. The good knower of people can be helped by classical "scientific" knowledge; the poor knower of people cannot be helped by all the abstract knowledge in the world. As some wit phrased it, "Any dope can have a high IQ."

## THE HOLISTIC APPROACH

I don't wish to hazard any large generalizations here, but this I have learned also (as a therapist and as personologist). If I want to learn somethimg more about you as an individual person, then I must approach you as a unit, as a one, as a whole. The customary scientific technique of dissection and reductive analysis that has worked so well in the inorganic world and not too badly even in the infrahuman world of living organisms, is just a nuisance when I seek knowledge of a person, and it has real deficiencies even for studying people in general. Psychologists have tried various atomistic dissections and reductions to fundamental building blocks of knowledge out of which, presumably, the whole was built—basic sensation bits, stimulus-response or associative bonds, reflex or conditioned reflexes, behavioral reactions, products of factor analysis, profiles of scores on various kinds of tests. Each of these efforts has left behind it some partial usefulness for the abstract, nomothetic science of psychology, but no one living would seriously propose any of them as a useful path to knowledge of members of a strange culture or of members of the John Birch Society, let alone of a blind date.

Not only must I perceive you holistically, but I must also analyze you holistically rather than reductively. (If I had the space, I should also like to spell out the effects of Gestalt psychology upon experimental and laboratory psychology; for a fuller treatment, see *38*, ch 3.)

SUBJECTIVE REPORT

By far the best way we have to learn what people are like is to get them, one way or another, to tell us, whether directly by question and answer or by free association, to which we simply listen, or indirectly by covert communications, paintings, dreams, stories, gestures, etc.—which we can interpret. Of course everyone knows this, and in our ordinary daily life all of us take advantage of this. But the fact remains that it raises real scientific problems. For example, a person who is telling us his political attitude is, so to speak, the only witness to what he is reporting. He can easily fool us if he wants to. An element of trust and good will and honesty is required here that is not required with any other existing object of scientific study. The interpersonal relationships of the speaker and of the listener are very much involved.

Astronomers, physicists, chemists, geologists, etc. need not concern themselves with such problems, at least not at first. It is possible for them to go far before needing to raise any questions about relationships between the knower and the known.

## RECEPTIVITY, NONINTERFERENCE; TAOISTIC SCIENCE

Most young psychologists have been taught to use the controlled experiment as the model way of acquiring knowledge. Slowly and painfully we psychologists have had to learn to become good clinical or naturalistic observers, to wait and watch and listen patiently, to keep our hands off, to refrain from being too active and brusque, too interfering and controlling, and—most important of all in trying to understand another person—to keep our mouths shut and our eyes and ears wide open.

This is different from the model way in which we approach physical objects, i.e., manipulating them, poking at them, to see what happens, taking them apart, etc. If you do this to human beings, you *won't* get to know them. They won't *want* you to know them. They won't *let* you know them. Our interfering makes knowledge less likely, at least at the beginning. Only when we already know a great deal can we become more active, more probing, more demanding—in a word, more experimental.

## PROBLEM-CENTERING AND METHOD-CENTERING: INSISTENCE ON HIGHER QUESTIONS

For me, the clash with method-centered scientists came only when I started asking questions about the so-called "higher life" of human beings and about more highly evolved human beings. So long as I worked behaviorally with dogs and monkeys and experimented with learning and conditioning and with motivated behavior, the available methodological tools served me well. These experiments could be suitably designed and controlled, and the data could be precise and reliable enough.

I got into real trouble only when I started asking new questions for the researcher, questions which I couldn't handle well, questions about imprecise, undefined, unmanageable problems. I discovered then that many scientists disdain what they cannot cope with, what they cannot do well. I remember counterattacking in my irritation with an aphorism I coined for the occasion: "What isn't worth doing, isn't worth doing well." Now I think I could add: "What needs doing, is worth doing even though *not* very well." Indeed, I am tempted to claim that the first effort to research a new problem is most likely to be inelegant, imprecise, and crude. What one mostly learns from such first efforts is how it should be done better the next time. But there is no way of bypassing this first time. I remember a child who, when told that most train accidents involved the last car, suggested that accidents could be reduced by eliminating last cars!

Neither can beginnings be eliminated. Even to think this, or to want it, is a denial of the very spirit of science. Cracking open new fields is certainly more exhilarating and rewarding and is also more socially useful. "You must love the questions themselves," Rilke said. The assault troops of science are certainly more necessary to science than its military policemen. This is so even though they are apt to get much dirtier and to suffer higher casualties. Bill Mauldin's cartoons during the war could serve as good illustrations of the clash in values between frontline fighting soldiers and rear echelon spit-and-polish officers. Somebody has to be the first one through the mine fields. (I wrote this first as "through the mind fields"!)

When my work in psychopathology led me to explore nonpathology—psychologically healthy people—difficulties came up that I had never had to face before, problems of values and of norms, for instance. Health is itself a normative word. I began to understand why so little had been done here. By the normal canons of good "normal" research, this was not a good research. (Actually I called it not a research, but an exploration.) It is easily criticized and I have done it too. There was a real question about the possible intrusion of my own values in the people I selected for study. A group of judges would have been better, of course. Today we have tests that are more objective and impartial than any unaided judgment—but in 1935 they didn't exist. It was either do it this way or not do it at all. I'm glad I chose to do it; I learned a great deal, and perhaps others have learned, too.

The study of these relatively healthy people and their characteristics opened up dozens of new problems for me both personally and as a scientist, and it made me dissatisfied with dozens of old solutions and methods and concepts that I had taken for granted. These people raised new questions about the nature of normality, of health, of goodness, of creativeness and love, of higher needs, beauty, curiosity, fulfillment, of heroes and the godlike in human beings, of altruism and cooperativeness, of love for the young, protection of the weak, compassion and unselfishness and humanitarianism, of greatness, of transcendent experiences, of higher values. (I have worked since with all of these questions, and I am confident that it is possible to contribute something toward answering them. They are not untestable, "unscientific" problems.)

These "higher" psychological processes in the human being did not fit gracefully and comfortably into the extant machinery for achieving reliable knowledge. This machine, it turned out, was much like something I have in my kitchen called a "disposall," which nevertheless does not really dispose of all things but only of some things. Or to make another comparison, I remember seeing an elaborate and complicated automatic washing machine for automobiles that did a beautiful job of washing them. But it could do *only* that, and everything else that got into its clutches was treated as if it were an automobile to be washed. I suppose it is tempting, if the only tool you have is a hammer, to treat everything as if it were a nail.

In a word, I had either to give up my questions or else to invent new ways of answering them. I preferred the latter course. And so also do many psychologists who choose to work as best they can with important problems (problem-centering) rather than restricting themselves to doing only that which they can do elegantly with the techniques already available (method-centering). If you define "science" as that which it is able to do, then that which it is not able to do becomes "nonscience," i.e., unscientific. (A fuller treatment of this problem is in *38,* ch. 2.)

### THE FEAR OF KNOWING; FEAR OF PERSONAL AND SOCIAL TRUTH

More than any other scientists we psychologists have to contend with the astonishing fact of resistance to the truth. More than any other kind of knowledge we fear knowledge of ourselves, knowledge that might transform our self-esteem and our self-image. A cat finds it easy to be a cat, as nearly as we can tell. It isn't afraid to be a cat. But being a full human being is difficult, frightening, and problematical. While human beings love knowledge and seek it—they are curious—they also fear it. The closer to the personal it is, the more they fear it. So human knowledge is apt to be a kind of dialectic between this love and this fear. Thus knowledge includes the defenses against itself, the repressions, the sugar-coatings, the inattentions, the forgettings. Therefore any methodology for getting at this truth must include some form of what psycho-analysts call "analysis of the resistance," a way of dissolving fear of the truth about oneself, thus permitting one to perceive himself head on, naked—a scary thing to do.

We can say something of the sort for knowledge in general. Darwin's theory of natural selection was a tremendous blow to the human ego. So also was the Copernican way of seeing things. And yet it is still true that there is a gradient of fear of knowledge; the more impersonal the knowledge, the less close to our personal concerns and to our emotions and needs, the less resistance to it there will be. And the closer our probings approach to our personal core, the more resistance there will be. There is a kind of "law of amount of knowledge" that we might phrase so: the greater the distance from personal knowledge, the greater the amount of scientific knowledge, the longer the history of the subject, the safer the study, the more mature the science, etc. And thus it comes about that we know (scientifically) far more about chemicals and metals and electricity than we do about sex or prejudice or exploitation.

One must sometimes talk to one's graduate students in the social and psychological sciences as if they were going off to war. One must speak of bravery, of morals and ethics, of strategy and tactics. The psychological or social scientist must *fight* to bring truth about the hot subjects.

### THE WISH TO BE KNOWN AND THE FEAR OF BEING KNOWN

The person is different from things as an object of knowledge in that he has to want to be known, or at least he has to permit himself to be known.[1] He must accept and trust the knower, and even get to love him in certain cases. He may even be said to surrender to the knower (*82*) in various senses of that term, and vice versa. It feels good to be understood

---

[1] When the person becomes an object of knowledge for himself, the situation becomes even more complicated. Generally it is better for him to have a skilled helper, which at once generates various subtle relationships between the person and his helper. How unusual this relationship may become was brought home to me dramatically in a psychotherapy class for psychiatric residents run by Dr. William Murphy, perhaps ten years ago. "I place upon my patients the fullest load of depression and anxiety that they are able to bear," he said. Remember this is a psychotherapist trying to understand his patient and also helping this person to know himself better.

(*73*), even exhilarating (*3*) and therapeutic. Other examples are scattered through this book (and through the whole literature of psychotherapy and social psychology).

## MOTIVATION, PURPOSES, ENDS

In dealing with persons, you must make your epistemological peace with the fact that people have purposes and goals of their own even though physical objects do not. Our classical science wisely tossed out of its study of the physical universe the projection of purposes, whether of a God or of man himself. As a matter of fact, this purging was a *sine qua non* for making physical science possible at all; the solar system is better understood so. The projection of purpose is not only unnecessary, it is actually harmful to full understanding.

But the case is completely different with human beings. They *do* have purposes and goals directly perceptible by introspection and also easily studied behaviorally, as in infrahuman animals (*71*). This simple fact, which is excluded systematically from the model of classical physical science, automatically makes its methods less appropriate for studying most human behavior. This is so because it does not differentiate between means and ends. Because of this, as Polanyi (*60*) points out, it cannot discriminate between correct and incorrect instrumental behavior, between efficient and inefficient, right and wrong, sick and healthy, since all these adjectives refer to the suitability and efficacy of the means-behavior in actually attaining its goal. Such considerations are alien to the

---

I am not sure that this was meant as an epistemological statement, but it most surely was just that. Granted that this relationship between knower and known is different from the more "normal" epistemological relationship between a histologist and the slides that he is studying, and granted also that the latter relationship has been the model one, yet I believe it is clear that theories of knower-known relationships must be broadened to cover the former as well as the latter.

purely physical or chemical system which has no purposes and therefore needs no discrimination between good or bad instrumental behaviors.

Our problems are further complicated by the fact that his purposes can be unknown to the person himself. For instance, his behavior can be what the psychoanalyst calls "acting out," i.e., an apparent seeking for an overtly discernible goal which, however, is not the "real" goal of the behavior but is rather a symbolic substitute that will never satisfy the hunger.

Any comprehensive psychology of science will have to go into great detail about the relations of consciousness to the unconscious and to the preconscious, and of so-called "primary process" cognition to "secondary process" cognition. We have learned to think of knowledge as verbal, explicit, articulated, rational, logical, structured, Aristotelian, realistic, sensible. Confronted with the depths of human nature, we psychologists learn to respect also the inarticulate, the preverbal and subverbal, the tacit, the ineffable, the mythic, the archaic, the symbolic, the poetic, the esthetic. Without these data, no account of a person can possibly be complete. But it is only in human beings that these data exist and for which, therefore, *ad hoc* methods have proved to be necessary. The rest of the book pursues this same question and some of its offshoots. How adequate or inadequate are the concepts and methods of classical science if our task is the acquisition of knowledge about the human person? What are the consequences of these inadequacies? What improvements do they suggest? What counterproposals can be offered for consideration and for testing? What can general science learn from person science?

# 3

# The Cognitive Needs Under Conditions of Fear and of Courage

Science has its origins in the needs to know and to understand (or explain), i.e., cognitive needs (*38, 43*). In another publication (*50*) I have summarized the various lines of evidence that make me feel these needs to be instinctlike and therefore defining characteristics of humanness (although not only of humanness), and of specieshood. In the same paper I tried to differentiate the cognitive activities instigated by anxiety and those that proceed without fear or by overcoming fear and can therefore be called "healthy." That is, these cognitive impulses seem to function under conditions *either* of fear or of courage, but they will have different characteristics under these two different conditions.

Curiosity, exploring, manipulating, when instigated by fear or anxiety, can be seen to have the primary goal of allaying anxiety. What looks behaviorally like an interest in the nature of the object being examined or the area being explored, may be primarily an effort by the organism to calm itself down and to lower the level of tension, vigilance, and apprehension. The unknown object is now primarily an anxiety-producer, and the behavior of examination and probing is first and foremost a detoxification of the object, making it into something that need not be feared. Some organisms, once reassured, may then go over into an examination of the object per se out of sheer, nonanxious curiosity in the independently existing reality out there. Other organisms may, however, lose all interest in the object once it is detoxified, familiarized (33), and no longer fearsome. That is to say, familiarization can produce inattention and boredom.

Phenomenologically these two kinds of curiosity feel different from each other. They are also different clinically and personologically. And finally they are also different behaviorally in several infrahuman species as well as in the human being, as many ingenious experiments have shown.

With human beings, we are irresistibly impelled by the same kinds of data to postulate another, "higher" concept beyond sheer curiosity. Different scholars have spoken variously of the need to understand, the need for meaning, the need for values, for a philosophy or a theory, or for a religion or cosmology, or for an explanatory or lawful "system" of some kind. These first approximations generally refer to some need to order, to structure, to organize, to abstract, or to simplify the chaotic multiplicity of facts. In most contexts, by contrast, the word "curiosity" can be interpreted as focusing upon a single fact, some single object, or at most a delimited set of objects or situations or processes rather than upon the whole world or large portions of it.

This need to understand, like its prepotent need to know, can also be seen as expressing itself and organizing behavior in the service of either allaying anxiety or nonanxious interest in the nature of reality. In both cases clinical and personological experience shows that anxiety and fear are generally prepotent over impersonal interest in the nature of reality. In this context "courage" can be seen as either absence of fear or as the ability to overcome the fear and to function well in spite of it.

Any cognitive activities, whether institutionalized ones like scientific work and philosophizing or personal ones like the search for insight in psychotherapy, can be better understood against this background. How much of anxiety and how much of anxiety-free interest are involved? Since most human activities are a mixture of both, what, we must ask, is the proportion of anxiety to courage? Behavior, including the behavior of the scientist, can be seen in simplest schema as a resultant of these two forces, that is, as a mixture of anxiety-allaying (defensive) devices and of problem-centered (coping) devices.

I have described this basic dialectic in several different ways in differing contexts. Each of these can be useful for different purposes. First of all (*34*, ch. 10, "Coping with Dangers") I made the distinction between the Freudian "defense mechanisms" (for allaying anxiety while still seeking gratification) and what I called "coping mechanisms" (for positive, courageous, and victorious solution of life problems in the absence of anxiety or in spite of it). Another useful distinction (*43*, ch. 3) is that between deficiency-motivations and growth-motivations. Cognition can be more one or more the other. Where it is primarily deficiency-motivated, it is more need-reductive, more homeostatic, more the relief of felt deficit. When behavior is more growth-motivated, it is less need-reductive and more a movement toward self-actualization and fuller humanness, more expressive, more selfless, more reality-centered. This is a little like saying, "Once we get our personal problems solved, then we can get truly interested in the world for its own sake."

Thirdly (*43*, ch. 4), growth was seen as an endless series of daily choices and decisions in each of which one can choose to go back toward safety or forward toward growth. Growth must be chosen again and again; fear must be overcome again and again.

In other words, the scientist can be seen as relatively defensive, deficiency-motivated, and safety-need-motivated, moved largely by anxiety and behaving in such a way as to allay it. Or he can be seen as having mastered his anxieties, as coping positively with problems in order to be victorious over them, as growth-motivated toward personal fulfillment and fullest humanness, and therefore as freed to turn outward toward an intrinsically fascinating reality, in wholehearted absorption with it rather than with its relevance to his personal emotional difficulties, i.e., he can be problem-centered rather than ego-centered.[1]

## THE PATHOLOGY OF COGNITION: ANXIETY-ALLAYING MECHANISMS IN COGNITION

Seeing this motivation at work in the most pathological instances demonstrates unmistakably that the search for knowledge can be anxiety-allaying.

First of all, let us examine briefly the brain-injured soldiers from whom Kurt Goldstein (22) learned so much. Their very real injuries and the real losses in capacity that ensued not only made them feel less capable but also made the world look more overwhelming. Much of their behavior could be understood as an attempt to retain self-esteem and to avoid anxiety-producing confrontation with problems from which they could expect only defeat. To this end they first of all

[1] "There are many ways of coping with such anxieties and some of these are cognitive. To such a person, the unfamiliar, the vaguely perceived, the mysterious, the hidden, the unexpected are all apt to be threatening. One way of rendering them familiar, predictable, manageable, controllable, i.e., unfrightening, and harmless, is to know them and to understand them. And so knowledge may have not only a growing-forward function, but also an anxiety-reducing function, a protective, homeostatic function. The overt behavior may be very similar, but the motivations may be extremely different. And the subjective consequences are then also different. On the one hand we have the sigh of relief, the feeling of lowered tension, let us say, of the worried householder exploring a mysterious and frightening noise downstairs in the middle of the night with a gun in his hand. This is quite different from the illumination and exhilaration, even the ecstasy, of a young student looking through a microscope who sees for

narrowed their worlds in order to avoid problems that they were incapable of handling and to restrict themselves to the problems they were capable of handling. Within such constricted worlds, daring less and trying less, being "modest" about aspirations and goals, they could function well. Secondly they ordered and structured these narrowed worlds carefully. They made a place for everything, and everything was in its place. They geometrized their little realms in an effort to make them predictable, controllable, and safe. Thirdly they tended to freeze them into static and unchanging forms and to avoid change and flux. Their worlds were thus made more predictable, more controllable, and less anxiety-producing.

For people who have limited capacities that they cannot trust, who see the world as too much for them, and who can't accept this state of affairs, these are sensible, logical, understandable things to do. They work. The soldiers' anxiety and pain were in fact reduced thereby. To the casual observer the patients looked normal.

That these safety-producing mechanisms are pragmatically sound (rather than "crazy" or weird and mysterious) can easily be seen from the close parallel with, let us say, newly

---

the first time the minute structure of a cell, or who suddenly understands a symphony or the meaning of an intricate poem or political theory. In the latter instances, one feels bigger, smarter, stronger, fuller, more capable, successful, more perceptive.

"This motivational dialectic can be seen on the largest human canvases, the great philosophies, the religious structures, the political and legal systems, the various sciences, even the culture as a whole. To put it very simply, *too* simply, they can represent simultaneously the outcome of the need to understand and the need for safety in varying proportions. Sometimes the safety needs can almost entirely bend the cognitive needs to their own anxiety-allaying purposes. The anxiety-free person can be more bold and more courageous and can explore and theorize for the sake of knowledge itself. It is certainly reasonable to assume that the latter is more likely to approach the truth, the real nature of things. A safety-philosophy or religion or science is more apt to be blind than a growth-philosophy, religion or science" (*43*, 61–62).

blinded people, who, because they are less capable than before, must also see the world as more dangerous, more overwhelming, and must at once elaborate all sorts of safety mechanisms to protect themselves from actual harm. So they at once have to narrow the world, perhaps confining themselves to their homes until they can get it "under control." Every piece of furniture must be fixed into place; everything must remain where it is. Nothing unpredicted or unexpected should happen; this is dangerous. The world must remain as it is. Change becomes dangerous. The routes from one place to another must be memorized by rote. All necessary objects must stay where they belong.

Something like this can be seen in compulsive-obsessive neurotics. A basic problem here seems to be, if I may oversimplify, a fear of the impulses and emotions within the person himself. Unconsciously he fears that if they should get out of control, terrible things might happen, murder perhaps. So on the one hand he keeps himself under tight control, and on the other hand he projects this intrapsychic drama on the world and tries also to control *it*. What he rejects within himself— emotion, impulsiveness, spontaneity, expressiveness—he rejects out there, too, although in an ambivalent way. As he rejects his inner voices and signals and consequently loses his trust in his spontaneous wishes and instinctlike impulses, he has to rely on external signals to tell him what to do and when to do it, e.g., calendars, clocks, schedules, agenda, quantifications, geometrizations, laws, rules of all sorts. Since change, flux, and unexpectedness may catch him with his controls down, he must also lay out the future, program it, make it exactly, make it predictable. His behavior also tends to get "organized" into repeatable rituals and ceremonials.

Here too we recognize the same safety-mechanisms. The obsessional person narrows his world by avoiding uncomfortable kinds of people, problems, impulses, and emotions, i.e., he lives a constricted life and tends to become a constricted person. He diminishes the world so that he may be able to control it. To avoid what he fears, he orders, regulates, and even freezes his world so that it can be predictable and therefore controllable. He tends to live "by the numbers," by the rule book, and to rely on external rather than internal cues, on logic and fact rather than on impulse, intuition, and emotion. (One obsessional patient once asked how he could prove that he was in love!)

The extreme hysterical neurotic, who is usually contrasted to the obsessional, is of less interest to us here because his massive repressions and denials *avoid* painful knowledge. It is hard to conceive of such a person being able to be a scientist at all, much less an engineer or technologist.

Finally we can learn from certain suspicious and paranoid people who compulsively need to know everything that is going on, i.e., who are afraid of not knowing. They have to know what is going on behind the closed door. The strange noise must be explained. The barely heard words must be fully heard. Danger lies in the unknown, and it stays dangerous so long as it is unknown. This knowledge-seeking behavior is primarily defensive. It is compulsive, inflexible, anxiety-instigated, and anxiety-producing. It is only apparently knowledge-seeking, because the reality, once it is known to be not dangerous, ceases to be interesting. That is, reality itself doesn't matter.

### OTHER COGNITIVE PATHOLOGIES

Some other sick (or primarily anxiety-instigated), clinically observed expressions of our needs to know and to understand (whether in scientist or lay knowers) can be listed:

1. The compulsive need for certainty (rather than the enjoyment and appreciation of it).

2. The premature generalization that so often is a consequence of the desperate need for certainty (because one cannot bear the state of waiting, of not knowing what the decision will be).

3. For the same reasons, desperately and stubbornly hanging on to a generalization, in spite of new information that contradicts it.

4. The denial of ignorance (for fear of looking stupid, weak, ludicrous)—the inability to say "I don't know," "I was wrong."

5. The denial of doubt, confusion, puzzlement: the need to appear decisive, certain, confident, sure of oneself; the inability to be humble.

6. The inflexible, neurotic need to be tough, powerful, fearless, strong, severe. Counterphobic mechanisms are defenses against fear, i.e., they are ways of denying that one is afraid when one really is afraid. Ultimately the fear of looking weak, soft, or mushy may turn out to be a defense against (misconceived and misinterpreted) femininity. Among scientists the legitimate wish to be "hard-nosed," or tough-minded, or rigorous may be pathologized into being "merely hard-nosed," or exclusively tough-minded, or of finding it impossible *not* to be rigorous. There may develop an inability to be gentle, surrendering, noncontrolling, patient, receptive even when the circumstances clearly call for it as prerequisite to better knowing, e.g., as in psychotherapy.

7. The ability to be only active, dominant, masterful, controlling, "in charge," "masculine," and the inability to be also noncontrolling, noninterfering, receptive. This is a loss of versatility in the knower.

8. Rationalization of the psychoanalytic sort ("I don't like that fellow and I'm going to find a good reason why").

9. Intolerance of ambiguity: the inability to be comfortable with the vague, the mysterious, the not yet fully known.

10. The need to conform, to win approval, to be a member of the group—the inability to disagree, to be unpopular, to stand alone. What this does to cognizing can be seen in the experiments of Asch (*4*), Crutchfield (*14*), and others.

11. Grandiosity, megalomania, arrogance, egotism, paranoid tendencies. Very often this turns out, in deep therapy, to be a defense against deeper lying feelings of weakness, worthlessness. In any case, this kind of ego gets in the way of a clear view of reality.

12. The *fear* of paranoia, grandiosity or hubris. Defenses against one's own pride, greatness, godlikeness. Lowering of levels of aspiration. Evasion of one's own growth. The inability to believe that one could discover something important, therefore blindness to such discoveries, disbelief in them, inability to rush in and exploit the discovery. Assigning oneself to trivial problems.

13. Overrespect for authority, for the great man. The need to keep his love. Becoming *only* a disciple, a loyal follower, ultimately a stooge, unable to be independent, unable to affirm himself. ("Don't be a Freudian; be a Freud." *"Don't* follow in the footsteps of the masters; seek their goals.")

14. Underrespect for authority. The need to fight authority. The inability to learn from one's elders or teachers.

15. The need to be always and only rational, sensible, logical, analytic, precise, intellectual, etc. Inability to be also nonrational, wild, crazy, intuitive, etc., when this is more suitable.

16. Intellectualization, i.e., transforming the emotional into the rational, perceiving only the intellectual aspect of complex situations, being satisfied with naming rather than experiencing, etc. This is a common shortcoming of professional intellectuals, who tend to be blinder to the emotional and impulsive side of life than to its cognitive aspects.

17. The intellect may be used as a tool for dominating, one-

up-manship, or for impressing people often at the cost of part of the truth.

18. Knowledge and truth may be feared, and therefore avoided or distorted, for many reasons (*43* ch. 5).

19. Rubricizing, i.e., pathological categorizing as a flight from concrete experiencing and cognizing (*38,* ch. 14).

20. Dichotomizing compulsively; two-valued orientation; either-or; black or white (*38,* 232-234).

21. The need for novelty and the devaluation of the familiar. The inability to perceive a miracle if it is repeated one hundred times. Devaluing what is already known, as, e.g., truisms, platitudes, etc.

And so on and so on. The list could be extended almost endlessly. For instance, *all* the Freudian defense mechanisms make for cognitive inefficiency, in addition to their other effects. Neuroses and psychoses in general can all be considered to be cognitive illnesses in addition to their other aspects. This is almost as true for the character disorders, the existential "disorders," the "value pathologies," and the diminishing, stunting, or loss of the human capacities. Even cultures and ideologies, many of them, can be analyzed from this point of view, e.g., as encouraging stupidity, as discouraging curiosity, etc.

The path to the full truth is a rocky one. Full knowing is difficult. This is true not only for the layman but also for the scientist. The main difference between him and the layman is that he has enlisted in this search for truth deliberately, willingly, and consciously and that he then proceeds to learn as much as he can about the techniques and ethics (*11*) of truth-seeking. Indeed, science in general can be considered a technique with which fallible men try to outwit their own human propensities to fear the truth, to avoid it, and to distort it.

The systematic study of the cognitive pathologies, then, would seem to be an obvious and normal part of scientific studies. Clearly such a branch of knowledge should help the scientist to become a better knower, a more efficient instrument. Why so little has been done in this direction is a puzzle.

## THE INTEGRATION OF CAUTIOUS KNOWING AND COURAGEOUS KNOWING

It seems, then, that these "good," "nice" scientific words—prediction, control, rigor, certainty, exactness, preciseness, neatness, orderliness, lawfulness, quantification, proof, explanation, validation, reliability, rationality, organization, etc. —are all capable of being pathologized when pushed to the extreme. All of them may be pressed into the service of the safety needs, i.e., they may become primarily anxiety-avoiding and anxiety-controlling mechanisms. They may be mechanisms for detoxifying a chaotic and frightening world *as well as* ways of loving and understanding a fascinating and beautiful world. Working for certainty or exactness or predictability, etc. may be either healthy or unhealthy, either defense-motivated or growth-motivated, and may lead either to the relief of anxiety or to the positive joy of discovery and understanding. Science can be a defense, *and* it can also be a path to the fullest self-actualization.

Just to make sure that a vital point be not misunderstood, we must also look at the courageous, growth-motivated, psychologically healthy scientist, again taking an extreme type for the moment in order to get sharp differentiations and contrasts. *All of these same mechanisms and goals are also found in the growth-motivated scientist.* The difference is that they are not neuroticized.[2] They are not compulsive, rigid, and

---

[2] See Horney's *Neurotic Personality Of Our Time* for excellent differentiations of the neurotic needs for love, safety, respect, etc. from healthy needs for love, safety, or respect.

uncontrollable, nor is anxiety produced when these rewards have to be postponed. They are not desperately needed, nor are they exclusively needed. It is possible for healthy scientists to enjoy not only the beauties of precision but also the pleasures of sloppiness, casualness, and ambiguity. They are able to enjoy rationality and logic but are also able to be pleasantly crazy, wild, or emotional. They are not afraid of hunches, intuitions, or improbable ideas. It is pleasant to be sensible, but it is also pleasant to ignore common sense occasionally. It is fun to discover lawfulness, and a neat set of experiments that solve a problem can and does produce peak-experiences. But puzzling, guessing, and making fantastic and playful surmises is also part of the scientific game and part of the fun of the chase. Contemplating an elegant line of reasoning or mathematical demonstrations can produce great esthetic and sacral experiences, but so also can the contemplation of the unfathomable.

All of this is exemplified in the greater versatility of the great scientist, of the creative, courageous, and bold scientists. This ability to be either controlled and/or uncontrolled, tight and/or loose, sensible and/or crazy, sober and/or playful seems to be characteristic not only of psychological health but also of scientific creativeness.

Ultimately, I am convinced, we shall have to include in the education of the young scientist both the techniques of caution and of boldness. Mere caution and soberness, mere compulsiveness can produce only good technicians who are much less likely to discover or to invent new truths or new theories. The caution, patience, and conservatism which are *sine qua non* for the scientist had better be supplemented by boldness and daring if creativeness is also the hope. Both are necessary. They need not be mutually exclusive. They can be integrated with each other. Taken together they constitute flexibility, adaptability, versatility. Or as psychoanalysts often say, the best psychoanalyst (or scientist or general human being) is the one who combines the good characteristics of the hysterical and of the obsessional, without having the bad characteristics of either.

From the epistemological point of view, if we accept the isomorphic and parallel interrelationships between knower and known (52), then we can confidently expect the "taller," bolder, more Olympian knower to be able to cognize higher truths. The merely cautious knower, avoiding everything that could produce anxiety, is partially blind. The world that he is able to know is smaller than the world that the strong man can know.

# 4

## Safety Science and Growth Science: Science as a Defense

Science, then, can be a defense. It can be primarily a safety philosophy, a security system, a complicated way of avoiding anxiety and upsetting problems. In the extreme instance it can be a way of avoiding life, a kind of self-cloistering. It can become—in the hands of some people, at least—a social institution with primarily defensive, conserving functions, ordering and stabilizing rather than discovering and renewing.

The greatest danger of such an extreme institutional position is that the enterprise may finally become functionally autonomous, like a kind of bureaucracy, forgetting its original purposes and goals and becoming a kind of Chinese Wall against innovation, creativeness, revolution, even against new truth itself if it is too upsetting. The bureaucrats may actually become covert enemies to the geniuses, as critics so often have been to poets, as ecclesiastics so often have been to the mystics and seers upon whom their churches were founded (*48*, ch. 4).

Taking it for granted that the function of science is not only revolutionary but also conserving, stabilizing, and organizing —like every social institution—how can the pathologizing of this conserving function be avoided? How can we keep it "normal," healthy, and fruitful? The essential answer is, I believe, about the same as the one in the previous chapter: to become more aware of the psychology of individual scientists, to realize fully their individual characterological differences, to recognize that any of the goals or methods or concepts of science can be pathologized either in the individual or in the social institution. If there are enough of these individuals, they may "capture" the institution and then label their constricting point of view "the philosophy of science."

This pulling and hauling between individuals is paralleled by a similar conflict within each individual. The struggle between fear and courage, between defense and growth, between pathology and health is an eternal, intrapsychic struggle. The great lesson we have learned from the pathology and therapy of this conflict within the individual is that to be on the side of courage, of growth and health, means also to be on the side of truth (especially since healthy courage and growth include healthy soberness, caution, and tough-mindedness).[1]

In other publications (*38, 43, 44, 49*) I have tried to demonstrate that dichotomizing is responsible for much of the pathologizing of thought. In contrast to thinking that is inclusive, integrative, and synergic, dichotomizing splits apart that which belongs together. What is left appears to be a whole and self-sufficient entity, but it is really separated and isolated pieces. Boldness and caution can be either dichotomized or integrated with each other. Boldness that remains integrated

[1] A personal note may help to keep a balance between these dialectical tendencies and to guard against the either-or choice of mutual exclusiveness that is almost a reflex in our society. In the psychoanalysis of my own intellectual and scientific life, I have found it necessary to avoid temptations from *both* overcaution and overcourage, overcontrol and overimpulsiveness. I think this kind of perpetual conflict, this necessity for daily choices between retreat and advance, conservation and boldness, etc., is a necessary and intrinsic part of the life of the scientist. Polanyi (*60*) has made this even clearer with his demonstrations that scientific knowledge is "personal," that it necessarily involves judgment, taste, faith, gambling, connoisseurship, commitment, responsibility.

with caution within the same person is very different from boldness *not* tempered with caution ("mere boldness"), which thereby turns into rashness and lack of judgment. The sensible caution of the healthily bold man is different from caution dichotomized from boldness, which is often a crippler and a paralyzer. The good scientist must be both versatile and adaptable, that is, he must be capable of caution and skepticism when they are called for and capable of daring when *it* is called for. This sounds like the not very helpful recommendation of the intuitive cook to add "not too much salt, not too little, but just the right amount." But the situation for the scientist is different because for him there is a way of judging the "right amount," namely, that which is best for discovering truth.[2]

## THE MATURE AND IMMATURE SCIENTIST

To some extent, the distinction between Kuhn's (*30*) normal scientist and his revolutionary one parallels the development from the adolescent to the adult male, or from immaturity to maturity. The boy's conception of what a man should be like is more embodied in the "normal" scientist, the obsessional character, the practical technologist, than it is in the great creator. If we could understand better the difference between the adolescent's misconception of maturity and actual maturity, we should thereby understand better the deep fear of creativeness and the counterphobic defenses against it. This in turn should illuminate the eternal struggle within each of us

[2] "Hysterical" and "schizoid tendencies" are both desirable standard equipment for the well-rounded, versatile, and flexible scientist (in whom they are not dichotomized from the rest of his personality and are therefore not pathologized). As I have already said, it is difficult to conceive of the extreme hysteric or the extreme schizophrenic as at all wanting to be a scientist or as able to be. The extreme obsessional *can* be a scientist of a certain kind, or at any rate, a technologist.

against our own self-actualization and our own highest destiny. The female version of immaturity, which is more apt to take a hysterical form, is less relevant to the formation of scientists.

The pre- and postadolescent boy is caught in a conflict between wanting to stay young and childish and also wanting to grow up. Childhood and maturity both have their pleasures and their disadvantages. In any case, both biology and society give him little choice. He is in fact growing biologically older, and society generally demands that he behave as the culture dictates.

So he has to tear himself loose—in our society at any rate —from his love for his mother. It is a force pulling him backward, and he fights it and her. He tries to achieve both independence and freedom from dependence on woman. He wants to join the company of men, to be the autonomous companion of his father rather than his dutiful, subordinated son. He sees men as being tough, fearless, impervious to discomfort and pain, independent of emotional ties, dominant, quick to anger and frightening in their anger, earthshakers, doers, builders, masters of the real world. All of this he tries to be. He drowns his fears and timidities—overdoing it, of course, with his counterphobic defenses—in an inability to refuse any challenge or dare. He enjoys striking fear into the hearts of all the little girls—and the big girls, too. He taboos his tenderness, his loving impulses, his compassion, his sympathy—all in the effort to be tough or at least to look tough. He fights the adults, the establishment, the authorities, and all the fathers, for the ultimate toughness is not to fear the father. He tries to throw his lifelong dominators (as he sees them) off his back and out of his own psyche while he still feels the yearning to depend on them. And of course the elders are, to some extent, real dominators and think of him as a child to take care of.

We can see these concepts incarnated and projected before our eyes, if we know where to look. For instance, we can find them made visible in the figure of the cowboy, of the tough delinquent or the gang leader, of the "Fearless Fosdick" type of detective, or of the G-man, or perhaps also many "sportsmen." To consider only one example, look at the acting-out and fantasy elements in the cowboy figure in the standard Western movie. The most obvious characteristics of the boy's dream of glory are all there. He is fearless, he is strong, he is "lone." He kills easily and in a magical, wish-fulfilling way: he never misses, and there is no blood, pain, or mess. Apart from his horse he doesn't love anyone, or at least he doesn't express it except in the most understated, implied, reverse-English way. Least of all does he have any romantic or tender love for women, who are either prostitutes or "good women." He is in every respect imaginable the far, polar opposite of the pansy type of homosexual in whose realm he includes all the arts, all of culture, all intellect, education, and civilization. These for him are all feminine, as are also cleanliness, emotion of any kind (except perhaps anger), facial expressions, orderliness, or religion. Fantasy cowboys never have children, nor do they have mothers or fathers or sisters (they may have brothers). Observe also the revealing fact that while there is much death, there is little or no blood, mutilation, or agony. And observe also that there is always a hierarchy of dominance, or pecking order, and the hero is always at the top of it.

The actually mature man, mature not only in years but also in personality development, is, to say it briefly, not threatened by his "weaknesses," by his emotions, by his impulses or cognitions. Therefore he is not threatened by what the adolescent would call "femininity" but what he would prefer to call humanness. He seems able to accept human nature, and therefore he doesn't have to fight against it within himself, he doesn't have to subdue portions of himself. A certain bull-fighter, is reputed to have said, "Sir, *anything* I do is masculine." This kind of acceptance of one's own nature instead of living up to some external ideal is characteristic of the more mature male who is so sure of himself that he doesn't have to bother proving anything. Openness to experience is characteristic. So also is postambivalence, i.e., being able to love wholly, without tinctures of hostility or fear or the necessity of control. To get a little closer to our topic I would also use the word for being able to give oneself over completely to an emotion, not only of love but also of anger, fascination, or total surrender to a scientific problem.

But just these characteristics of emotional maturity correlate highly with the characteristics of the creative man that have so far been discovered (I won't say "eminent" or "talented" men; that can be quite different). For instance, Richard Craig (*13*) has demonstrated an almost complete overlap between the personality characteristics of creative men listed by Torrance (*72*) and those that I had listed for self-actualizing people (*38*). The two concepts in fact seem almost to be the same.

Which characteristics of average scientists might be expressions of immaturity and are therefore to be worried about and examined closely? There are many that are relevant, but a single example will do. Let us examine one excessive emphasis on controlling and excluding in the senses that I have described for adolescents. These latter suppress and exclude whatever they fear looks weak or feminine. So also the overdefensive or overobsessional or "immature" scientists, in accordance with his basic dynamics of mistrusting his impulses and his emotions and in his stress on control, tends to exclude, to set up hurdles and to close doors, to be suspicious. He is apt to dislike lack of control in others as well and to dislike impulsiveness, enthusiasm, whimsicality, and unpredictability. He is apt to be cool, sober, and stern. He is apt to prefer toughness and coolness in science to the point of synonymizing them. Clearly, such considerations are relevant and should be researched far more than they have.

# 5

## Prediction and Control of Persons?

The ultimate goals of knowledge about persons are different from the goals of knowledge about things and animals. It makes a certain sense to talk about prediction and control as exclusive desiderata when we speak of molecules or paramecia or domestic animals, although I would argue it even there. But how could it seriously be said that our efforts to know human beings are for the sake of prediction and control? The opposite is more often the case—that we would be horrified by this possibility of prediction and control. If humanistic science may be said to have any goals beyond sheer fascination with the human mystery and enjoyment of it, these would be to release the person from external controls and to make him *less* predictable to the observer (to make him freer, more creative, more inner-determined) even though perhaps more predictable to himself.

And as for the goals of self-knowledge, that is still a different and even more complex story. Self-knowledge is first and foremost, for no sake other than itself. It is intrinsically fascinating. It feels good and tastes good (in the long run, at least). And also we have been assured in our time that even when it is a painful process, it is the preferred path to the removal of symptoms. It is a way of removing unnecessary anxiety, depression, and fear. It is a means to the end of feeling good. Even, we have learned, the nineteenth-century goal of self-control (that in any case was through will power, not self-knowledge) is being replaced by the notion of spontaneity, almost the opposite of the older concept of self-control. What this means is that if we know our own biological nature, i.e., the intrinsic self, well enough, then this knowledge indicates to us our personal destiny. That is, it implies that we would love our own nature and would yield to it, enjoy it, and express it fully if only we knew it well enough. In turn this implies a rejection of many historical philosophies of the good life. The way to be a good person, for most Western philosophers and religionists, has been to control and suppress the lower, animal biological nature.

But the spontaneity theory of the humanistic psychologists implies a profoundly different schema (the model instance to which the exceptions are peripheral instances). The most basic impulses are *not* seen as necessarily evil or dangerous in themselves. The problems of expression and gratification of these impulses are essentially problems of strategy rather than of right and wrong or of good and evil. The "controls" upon need expression and need gratification now become questions of how best to gratify, when to gratify, where and in what style. Such "Apollonizing" controls do not call the needs into question. And I would go so far as to say that any environment or culture that does call them into question, that makes a permanent ethical problem of sex, hunger, love, self-respect, etc., may be suspected a priori of being a "bad" society.

The upshot is that the word "control" can have a different meaning for humanists, one synergic with impulse, not in contradiction to it. This meaning enables us to say that the goal of self-knowledge is closer to what we call freedom than it is to suppressive self-control.

So also for predictability. This too seems to undergo great

changes in definition when applied to knowledge of self or of a person. This too can be studied empirically by studying people after therapy, people in their fully human moments, etc.

## PREDICTABILITY AS A GOAL

The word "predictable" as customarily used means "predictable by the scientist" and also carries the implication of "control by the scientist." It is interesting that when I *can* predict what a person will do under certain circumstances, this person tends to resent it. Somehow he feels that it implies a lack of respect for him, as if he were not his own master, as if he couldn't control himself, as if he were no more than a thing. He tends to feel dominated, controlled, outwitted (*43*, ch. 9).

I have observed instances of a person deliberately upsetting the predictions simply to reaffirm his unpredictability and therefore autonomy and self-governance. For instance, a ten-year-old girl, known for being always a good citizen, law-abiding and dutiful unexpectedly disrupted classroom discipline by passing out French fried potatoes instead of notebooks simply because, as she later said, everyone just took her good behavior for granted. A young man who heard his fiancée say of him that he was so methodical that she always knew what to expect of him, deliberately did what was not expected of him. Somehow he felt her statement to be insulting. Being predictable is often a sign of severe pathology. Goldstein's brain-injured soldiers (*22*), for instance, could be easily manipulated because of their predictable responses to certain stimuli: being stimulus-bound means being both predictable and controllable.

And yet we also use the word in a complimentary way: "You can really count on him in an emergency"; "He'll always come through in a pinch"; "I would stake my life on his honesty." We seem to wish for continuity in the basic structure of the personality but not in all its details.

The goal of predictability is even more complex if we consider self-knowledge. There seems to be a parallel to the fact that self-knowledge decreases control from outside the person and increases control from within the person, i.e., less other-determined and more self-determined. As self-knowledge increases, it certainly seems to increase self-predictability, at least where important and basic issues are concerned. And yet this may mean being less predictable to others in many ways.

Finally I want to add a few words about these concepts of prediction, control, and understanding at the highest level that we now know, that is, at the Being level (48). At this level the Being values have become incorporated into the self. Indeed they have become defining characteristics of the self. Truth, justice, goodness, beauty, order, unity, comprehensiveness, etc. have now become metaneeds, thereby transcending the dichotomy between selfish and unselfish, between personal needs and impersonal desiderata.

Freedom has now become Spinozistic, i.e., the freedom to embrace and to love one's own destiny, which is certainly determined at least in part by the discovery and the understanding of what and who one is, of one's Real Self (à la Horney), and of being eager to surrender to it. This is to let *it* control, to choose freely to be determined by it; thus it is to transcend the dichotomies "freedom *vs.* determinism" or "freedom *vs.* control" or "understanding as a goal *vs.* prediction and control as goals."

The meanings of these words shift and to some extent approach merging with each other in ways that demand careful study.

In any case, by now one thing must be clear. The simplistic conceptions of "prediction" and "control" that were suitable to a Newtonian "billiard-table" (matter in motion) conception of science are left behind as soon as we get to the humanistic and transhumanistic levels of science.

# 6

## Experiential Knowledge and Spectator Knowledge

Many things in life cannot be transmitted well by words, concepts, or books. Colors that we see cannot be described to a man born blind. Only a swimmer knows how swimming feels; the nonswimmer can get only the faintest idea of it with all the words and books in the world. The psychopath will never know the happiness of love. The youngster must wait until he is a parent in order to know parenthood fully and to say "I didn't realize." My toothache feels different from your toothache. And so it goes. Perhaps it is better to say that all of life must first be known experientially. There is no substitute for experience, none at all.[1] All the other paraphernalia of communication and of knowledge—words, labels, concepts,

[1] This world of experience can be described with two languages, a subjective, phenomenological one and an objective, "naïvely realistic" one, as Niels Bohr pointed out long ago. Each one can be close to the language of everyday life, and yet neither describes life completely. Each has its uses and both are necessary. Psychotherapists have long since learned to differentiate these languages and to use them differently. For instance, in the analysis of interpersonal relationships, they try to teach their patients to say, in a nonblaming, nonprojecting way, "Somehow in your presence I feel small" (or "rejected," or "angry," etc.) rather than saying "You don't like me," "You think you're better than I am," "Stop trying to dominate me," or "Why do you enjoy making me feel stupid?" That is, they teach them to experience their emotions as being inside themselves rather than automatically projecting them outward, as most people do. This obviously important differentiation is too huge to pursue any further here.

symbols, theories, formulas, sciences—all are useful only because people already know experientially. The basic coin in the realm of knowing is direct, intimate, experiential knowing. Everything else can be likened to banks and bankers, to accounting systems and checks and paper money, which are useless unless there is real wealth to exchange, to manipulate, to accumulate, and to order.

It is easy to carry this simple truth beyond its proper limits. For instance, while it is mostly true that the color red cannot be described to a congenitally blind man, yet this does not mean that words are useless, as some are prone to conclude. Words are fine for communicating and sharing experiences with those who have already experienced. Alcoholics Anonymous, Gamblers Anonymous, Synanon, and similiar groups of people who have "been there" prove both points: first, that words fail before lack of experience; and second, that they are quite good between people who have shared an experience (*48*, Appendix on rhapsodic communication). Daughters must wait until they themselves give birth before being able to "understand" their mothers and to be fully friendly with them. Even more, words and concepts are absolutely necessary for organizing and ordering the welter of experiences and the ultraexperiential world of which they apprise us. (Northrop [*59*] is especially good on this point.)

If we add to these considerations the whole world of the primary processes, of the unconscious and preconscious, of metaphorical communications, and of the nonverbal communications—as between two dancing partners, let us say—we get a further enrichment of the total picture, namely, that experiential knowledge is *sine qua non* but not all, i.e., it is necessary but not sufficient. Also we avoid thereby the trap of dichotomizing experiential knowledge from and against conceptual knowledge. My thesis is that experiential knowledge is prior to verbal-conceptual knowledge but that they are hierarchically-integrated and need each other. No human being dare specialize too much in either kind of knowing. Science with the psyche left in can be shown to be more powerful than the science which excludes experiential data.

Nor need these affirmations in any way contradict a "minimal" behaviorism, that is, a doctrine of levels in the reliability of knowledge in which public knowledge is granted to be more trustworthy and more constant for many purposes than private and subjective knowledge. Psychologists are only too aware of the shortcomings and even impossibility of a pure and sole introspectionism. We know too much of hallucinations, delusions, illusions, denials, repressions, and other defenses against knowing reality. Since you don't have my repressions or my illusions, comparing my subjective experience with your subjective experience is an easy and obvious way of filtering out the distorting power of my intrapsychic defensive forces. One might call this the easiest kind of reality-testing. It is a first step toward checking knowledge by making sure it is shared, i.e., that it is not a hallucination.

This is why I can think that (1) most psychological problems do and should begin with phenomenology rather than with objective, experimental, behavioral laboratory techniques, and also (2) that we must usually press on from phenomenological beginnings *toward* objective, experimental, behavioral laboratory methods. This is I think a normal and usual path—from a less reliable beginning toward a more reliable level of knowledge. To begin the scientific study of love, for instance, with physicalistic methods would be to be meticulous about something only crudely known, like exploring a continent with a pair of tweezers and a magnifying glass. But also to restrict oneself to phenomenological methods is to be content with a lower degree of certainty and reliability than is actually attainable.

### THE GOOD KNOWER

The last few decades of clinical and experimental psychology have brought into clearer focus the logically prior need, before knowing, to be a good knower. The distorting power not only of the various psychopathologies but also of the more "normal" ungratified needs, hidden fears, characteristic defenses, i.e., of the "normal" or average personality, are far greater than mankind ever thought before this century. In my opinion we have learned from clinical and personological experience (1) that improvement of psychological health makes the person a better knower, even a better scientist, and (2) that a very good path to improved and fuller humanness or health has been via self-knowledge, insight, and honesty with oneself.

In effect what I am implying is that honest knowing of oneself is logically and psychologically prior to knowing the extrapsychic world. Experiential knowledge is prior to spectator knowledge. If you want to see the world, it is obviously sensible to be as good a seer as you can make yourself. The injunction might read, then: make yourself into a good instrument of knowledge. Cleanse yourself as you would the lenses of your microscope. Become as fearless as you can, as honest, authentic and ego-transcending as you can. Just as most people (or scientists) are not as fearless, ego-transcending, honest, unselfish, or dedicated as they could be, so most people are not as efficient cognizers as they are capable of becoming.

(I pause only to ask the question: What might all this mean for the education of scientists and for the scientific education of nonscientists? Even asking the question is enough to make us doubtful about what is called science education.)

But the statement must be rounded out. We can't stop there. It is all very well to be honest, authentic, decent. But beyond honesty, what? Authenticity is not the same as knowledge, any more than a clean microscope is. It is fine to be honest, in fact it is prerequisite and *sine qua non* to being a good scientist. But it is also necessary to become skilled, competent, professional, knowledgeable, learned. Health is necessary but not sufficient for the would-be knower and doer.

That is to say, experiential knowledge is not enough. Self-knowledge and self-improvement are not enough. The task of knowing the world and of being competent within it still remains, and therefore also does the task of accumulating and ordering knowledge-about, that is, spectator knowledge, knowledge of the nonhuman.

I hope I make myself clear. Again I have been substituting a hierarchical integration for a dichotomous antagonism. The two kinds of knowledge are necessary to each other and under good circumstances can be and should be intimately integrated with each other.

## SPECTATOR KNOWLEDGE ABOUT THINGS

What does the orthodox scientist mean by "knowing"? Let us remember that at the beginning of science the word "knowing" meant "knowing of the external physical world," and for the orthodox scientist it still does. It means looking at something that is not you, not human, not personal, something independent of you the perceiver. It is something to which you are a stranger, a bystander, a member of the audience. You the observer are, then, really alien to it, uncomprehending and without sympathy and identification, without any starting point of tacit knowledge that you might already have. You look through the microscope or the telescope as through a keyhole, peering, peeping, from a distance, from outside, not as one who has a right to be in the room being peeped into. Such a scientific observer is not a participant observer. His science can be likened to a spectator sport, and he to a spectator. He has no necessary involvement with what he is looking at, no loyalties, no stake in it. He can be cool, detached, emotionless, desireless, wholly other than what he is looking at. He is in the grandstand looking down upon the goings on in the arena; he himself is not in the arena. And ideally he doesn't care who wins.

He can be and should be neutral if he is looking at something utterly strange to him. It is best for the veridicality of his observations that he lay no bets, be neither for nor against, have no hopes or wishes for one outcome rather than another. It is most efficient, if he seeks a truthful report, that he move toward being nonaligned and uninvolved. Of course we know that such neutrality and noninvolvement is theoretically almost impossible. Yet movement *toward* such an ideal is possible, and is different from movement *away* from it.

It will help communication with those who have read Martin Buber if I call this I-It knowledge by contrast with the I-Thou knowledge that I shall try to describe. I-It knowledge is sometimes all you can do with things, with objects that have no human qualities to be identified with and to be understanding about. See also Sorokin (*69*, 287), who comes to similar conclusions from a different starting point.

I do not mean here that this alien knowledge of the alien is the best that can be managed, even for things and objects. More sensitive observers are able to incorporate more of the world into the self, i.e., they are able to identify and empathize with wider and wider and more and more inclusive circles of living and nonliving things. As a matter of fact, this may turn out to be a distinguishing mark of the highly matured personality. It is likely that some degree of such identification makes possible some corresponding degree of experiential knowledge, by becoming and *being* what is to be known rather than remaining totally the outside spectator.

Since this identification can be subsumed under "love" broadly defined, its ability to increase knowledge from within may be considered for research purposes an instance of improvement of knowledge by love. Or perhaps we might formulate a general hypothesis to read so: love for the object seems likely to enhance experiential knowledge of the object, with lack of love diminishing experiential knowledge of the object, although it may very well increase spectator knowledge of that same object.

An obvious illustration supported by common sense experience might be this. Researcher A is really fascinated with schizophrenics (or white rats or lichens). Researcher B, however, is much more interested in manic-depressive insanity (or monkeys or mushrooms). We may confidently expect that Researcher A will (a) freely choose or prefer to study schizophrenics, etc., (b) work better and longer at it, be more patient, more stubborn, more tolerant of associated chores, (c) have more hunches, intuitions, dreams, illumination about them, (d) be more likely to make more profound discoveries about schizophrenia, and (e) the schizophrenics will feel easier with him and say that he "understands" them. In all these respects he would almost certainly do better than Researcher B. But observe that this superiority is in principle far greater for acquiring experiential knowledge than it is for acquiring knowledge about something, or spectator knowledge, even though Researcher A probably could do a bit better at that, too.

So far as spectator knowledge of the alien is concerned, any competent scientist or research assistant may confidently be expected to accumulate knowledge about *anything* in a normal, routine way, e.g., external statistics. As a matter of fact, this is exactly what happens a great deal today in an age of "projects," grants, teams, and organizations. Many scientists can be hired to do one disconnected, passionless job after another, just as a good salesman prides himself on being able to sell anything, whether he likes it or not, or as a horse pulls whatever wagon he happens to get hitched to.

This is one way of describing the Cartesian split between the knower and the known that the existentialists, for instance, speak of today. We might also call it the "distancing" or perhaps even the alienation of the knower from his known. It must be clear from what has gone before that I can conceive of other kinds of relationships between knower and known or between perceiver and percept. I-Thou knowledge, knowledge by experiencing, knowledge from within, love knowledge, Being-Cognition, fusion knowledge, identification knowledge —all these have been or will be mentioned. Not only do these other forms of knowing exist, but also they are actually better, more efficacious, more productive of reliable and valid knowledge *if* we are trying to acquire knowledge of a particular person or even persons in general. If we wish to learn more about persons, then this is the way we'd better go about it.

### SOME PROPERTIES AND CHARACTERISTICS OF EXPERIENCING[2]

Fullest and richest experiencing of the kind described by the Zen Buddhists, the general semanticists, and the phenomenologists includes at least the following aspects (my own primary source of data here are studies of peak experiences):

1. The good experiencer gets "utterly lost in the present," to use Sylvia Ashton-Warner's beautiful phrase. He loses his past and his future for the time being and lives totally in the here-now experience. He is "all there," immersed, concentrated, fascinated.

2. Self-consciousness is lost for the moment.

[2] A much fuller treatment of this topic is available in *45*.

3. The experiencing is timeless, placeless, societyless, historyless.

4.  In the fullest experiencing a kind of melting together of the person experiencing with that which is experienced occurs. This is difficult to put into words but I shall try below.

5. The experiencer becomes more "innocent," more receptive without questioning, as children are. In the purest extreme the person is naked in the situation, guileless, without expectations or worries of any kind, without "shoulds" or "oughts," without filtering the experience through any a priori ideas of what the experience should be, or of what is normal, correct, proper, right. The innocent child receives whatever happens without astonishment, shock, indignation, or denial and without any impulse to "improve" it. The full experience inundates the "helpless," will-less, amazed, and unselfishly interested experiencer.

6. One especially important aspect of full experiencing is the abeyance of importance-unimportance. Ideally the experience is not structured into relatively important or unimportant aspects, central or peripheral, essential or expendable.

7. In the good instance fear disappears (along with all other personal or selfish considerations). The person is then nondefensive. The experience rushes in upon him without hindrance.

8. Striving, willing, straining tend to disappear. Experience happens without being made to happen.

9. Criticism, editing, checking of credentials or passports, skepticism, selecting and rejecting, evaluating—all tend to diminish or, in the ideal, to disappear for the time being, to be postponed.

10. This is the same as accepting, receiving, being passively seduced or raped by the experience, trusting it, letting it happen, being without will, noninterfering, surrendering (*82*).

11. All of this adds up to laying aside all the characteristics of our most prideful rationality, our words, our analysis, our ability to dissect, to classify, to define, to be logical. All of these processes are postponed. To the extent that they intrude, to that extent is the experience less "full." Experiencing of this sort is much closer to Freud's primary process than to his secondary processes. It is in this sense nonrational—although it is by no means antirational.[3]

## THE PERSON AS SUBJECTIVELY ACTIVE OR PASSIVE

One trouble with classical science applied to psychology is that all it knows how to do well is to study people as objects, when what we need is to be able to study them also as subjects.

To be a passive spectator of ourselves and our own subjective processes is to be like a spectator at a movie. Something is happening to us; we are not making it happen. We do not have the feeling of willing it to happen. We simply observe.

The feeling of being an active subject (or agent) is quite different. We are involved, we try, we strive, we make efforts and we get tired, we can succeed or fail, we can feel strong or weak, when, for instance, we try to recall, to understand, to solve a problem, to call up an image deliberately. These are the experiences of willing, of being responsible, of being a prime mover, of being able, of being in command of oneself, self-determined rather than other-determined, caused, helpless, dependent, passive, weak, unable, bossed, commanded,

[3] A simple example of the way in which experiencing meshes with rationality is seen in the technique of "brainstorming," in which criticism is postponed to a second stage after all the crazy and wild ideas have been permitted to emerge. Very similar is the Primary Rule of psychoanalysis. The patient is taught not to select from or edit his free associations, as they emerge into consciousness and into speech. After they have been said out loud, they can then be examined, discussed, criticized. This is an example of the way in which "experiencing" is a cognitive tool for finding portions of the truth which other methods fail to find.

or manipulated (*43*, 100). Apparently, some people are not aware of having such experiences or have them only weakly, although I am sure it would be possible to teach an average person to be conscious of such experiencing.

Difficult or not, it has to be done. Otherwise we shall be unable to understand the concepts variously called individuation, the real self, self-actualization, and identity. Furthermore we shall never be able to make any headway with the phenomena of willing, spontaneity, fully functioning, responsibility, self-esteem, and confidence. Ultimately, this stress on man as active subject makes possible the image of man as an initiator, a creator, a center of action, as one who does things rather than one who is done to.

The various behaviorisms all seem to generate inexorably such a passive image of a helpless man, one who (or should I say "which"?) has little to say about his (its?) own fate, who doesn't decide anything. Perhaps it is this ultimate philosophical consequence that makes all such psychologies totally unacceptable to so many—because they neglect what is so richly and undeniably experienced. And it does no good to cite here the ways in which common sense perceptions are contradicted by scientific knowledge, e.g., the sun circling the earth. It is not a real parallel. My crucially important experience of being an active subject is—depending on the comprehensiveness of the objectivism—either denied altogether or is melted down into stimuli and responses, or is simply pushed aside as "unscientific," i.e., beyond respectable scientific treatment. An accurate parallel would be either to deny the existence of the sun, to insist that it was really something else, or else to deny that it could be studied.

All these errors would be avoided if the people who espouse positivism and behaviorism were not so often too sweeping, too doctrinaire, too monistic, too excluding. I have no doubt that objective, measurable, recordable, repeatable movements or responses are often more reliable, more trust-worthy forms of knowledge than are subjective observations. Neither am I in any doubt about the frequent desirability, as a strategy, of moving in this direction nor about anyone's right to prefer it. Today we must study anxiety, depression, or happiness mostly as private experiences and verbal reports. But this is because we can't do any better today. On the day when we discover an externally and publicly observable and measurable correlate of anxiety or of happiness, something like a thermometer or a barometer, on that day a new era in psychology will have begun. Since I think this is not only desirable but possible, I have pressed in this direction. This amounts to seeing data as arranged in a hierarchy of greater and lesser reliability, a hierarchy of knowledge that parallels an equally necessary idea of "stages or levels of development of science."[3]

Such an approach is quite compatible with a problem-centered orientation and with an experiential psychology, a self-psychology, etc. It is, so to speak, an open-door policy rather than an excluding policy in science, a tolerant pluralism rather than a "true faith." Any question can be asked, any problem raised. Once it is raised, you go on from there to do the best you can to get the answer to that particular question,

---

[3] It was said of a certain book in an unintentionally amusing way that it was "a forthright, courageous and highly rigorous study on the difficult problem of woman's sexuality, about which so little is known." Could it possibly be more clear that the word "known" is used here in a special sense, a sense that is chosen but that is not the only possible choice? In the experiential sense it is hard to think of anything better known than female sexuality. Has any phenomenon evoked more curiosity, speculation, theorizing, and careful and loving investigation and personal attention? And will any verbal description be of much use until personal experiencing has occurred? And yet this same example will serve beautifully to show not only that experiential knowledge is prepotent to abstract knowledge but also how limited *mere* experiential knowledge can be. This statement is correct if it refers to shared, public, structured, organized knowledge. There is in truth little "developed scientific knowledge" of female sexuality, although there could easily be.

the solution to that particular problem, without permitting yourself to be hampered by any conceptual or methodological pieties that might forbid you to use all your wits, all your capacities in the enterprise. One could almost say at such a moment that there are no rules, at least none that is binding a priori. Methods must be created as necessary, and so also must any heuristic framework of definition and concept that may be useful or necessary. The only requirement is to do the best you can with the problem at the time and under the circumstances.[4] Certainly *I* would not care to give instructions about how to tackle all future problems, and certainly I wouldn't give much respect to the doctrinaire scientist who assumes in effect that what was good enough for his daddy is good enough for him.

Nor do I wish to imply that a scientist may not choose the limited objectives and aspirations of classical science if he wishes. Some people dislike skating on thin ice. And why should they not do as they please? It would be a blow to science if all scientists preferred the same problem, the same method, the same philosophy, just as it would be a deathblow to the orchestra if everyone preferred to play the oboe. Clearly science is a collaboration, a division of labor, and no single man is responsible for the whole of it, nor could he be. No, this is not the issue. Rather it is the tendency to get pious and metaphysical about these personal preferences and to exalt them into rules for everyone else. It is the insistence on generating sweeping and excluding philosophies of knowledge, of truth, and therefore of human nature that makes trouble. This is hard to make clear, as I discovered long ago when I tried to argue with a woman who lived exclusively on Brazil nuts and cabbage. It was all useless because she concluded only that I

---

[4] "The scientific method, as far as it is a method, is nothing more than doing one's damndest with one's mind, no holds barred" (Percy Bridgman, *8*).

was "prejudiced" against nuts and cabbage. Or, to the same point, we can share the bafflement of the man whose mother gave him two ties for his birthday. He put one on to please her, only to be asked, "Why do you hate the other tie?"

### A LESSON FROM SYNANON

Inductive knowledge can never bring certainty. It can only generate higher subjective and objective probabilities. But in a real sense experiential knowledge can be certain and perhaps even is the only certainty, as so many philosophers have thought (passing over, for the moment, the question of mathematical certainty). In any case, it is real and, at times, certain for the psychotherapist.

Of course, such statements are debatable, resting as heavily as they do on particular definitions of particular words. It is not necessary to enter upon these debates here. And yet it should be possible to convey some of the operational meanings to which such statements refer, since they are indubitable to most clinical psychologists, psychiatrists, therapists, and personologists. If these meanings can be communicated, this should contribute to greater understanding between scientists of the personal and of the impersonal.

The mode of operation of Synanon, Alcoholics Anonymous, "street-corner workers," and other similar groups can supply us with excellent examples. These subcultures work on the principle that only a (cured) drug addict or alcoholic can fully understand, communicate with, help, and cure another drug addict or alcoholic. Only the one who *knows* is accepted at all by addicts. Addicts permit themselves to be known only by addicts. Furthermore only addicts passionately want to cure addicts.[5] Nobody else loves them enough and under-

[5] Is all therapy self-therapy? Do they want to keep on curing themselves? Do they *need* to? Is this a way of giving oneself love and forgiveness? of

stands them enough. As they themselves say, "Only somebody who has been through the same mill really *knows*."

One major consequence of having shared the experience and of knowing it from within is the great sureness and skill that permits one of the ultimate tests of knowledge, namely, the ability to inflict helpful pain without fear, without guilt, without conflict or ambivalence. I have pointed out elsewhere (*46*) that the perception of oughtness and requiredness is an intrinsic consequence of clearly perceived realness and sureness of knowledge, and that decisiveness and sure action, relentless and tough if need be, is a kind of Socratic consequence of "ought-perception." (Socrates taught that ultimately evil behavior can come only from ignorance. Here I am suggesting that good behavior needs as a precondition good knowledge and is perhaps a necessary consequence of good knowledge.) That is, from sureness of knowledge—and from the fact that some kinds of sureness of knowledge can come only from experiencing—comes effective, successful, efficient, decisive, stern, strong, unambivalent action.

It is precisely this kind of action—and perhaps only this kind of action—that can help addicts because their way of life so often rests on "conning" others, on false tears and promises, on seducing and ingratiating, on wearing a false front, on fooling people with it and therefore feeling contempt for them. Only other addicts, who know, cannot be fooled. I have seen them in the process of contemptuously, brutally, obscenely ripping away this false front, the hitherto accepted lies and promises, the successful defenses, the phony mask that formerly worked so well. I have seen the experienced ones laughing at

---

embracing one's past and assimilating it, transforming it into something good? Does this not suggest that other helping activities, e.g., psychotherapy, education, parenthood, may possibly be seen in a new light with the aid of this paradigm? And does not this possibility in turn suggest the great question, "To what extent is *any* personal and interpersonal knowing a knowing by identification, i.e., a self-knowing? How useful is such a point of view?"

the tears, touching and poignant to the inexperienced spectator but soon exposed as fake, maudlin, guileful. To date this is
the only way that works. This seeming harshness is pragmatically "called for." It is therefore ultimately compassionate
rather than sadistic. It is far more truly loving than the lack
of sternness which is falsely labeled affection, which creates
the addict, and which "supports his habit" rather than letting
him become strong enough to go away. In this subsociety the
contempt for social workers, psychiatrists, and other "experts"
is thick and heavy. There is a total mistrust and hatred and
sometimes fear of "mere" book knowledge, of people with
degrees, of people who are certified as knowing but who in
fact know nothing. This itself is probably a potent dynamic
factor in helping to maintain this "world."

In this realm spectator knowledge is unmistakeably different from and opposed to experiential knowledge, and it is
clearly far less effective. And because this difference makes a
difference, it is thereby proved to be real.

If I may milk still another moral from this experience, I
would like to call attention to the lunatic fact that as nearly as
I can make out, the Synanon type of treatment cures many
of its addicts, while our whole apparatus of hospitals,
physicians, police, prisons, psychiatrists, and social workers
cures practically none. But this ineffective and perhaps worse
than useless apparatus has the complete support of the whole
society, of all the professions, and eats up huge amounts of
money. The effective method, as nearly as I, a lay observer,
can make out, gets practically no money at all, no official
support, and indeed it is officially neglected or opposed by all
the professions, by the government, by the foundations.
Former drug addicts normally do not have degrees and professional training for obvious reasons, and therefore they do not
have "standing" and "status" in the conventional world. Thus
they cannot get jobs, money, or backing in spite of the clear

fact that they are the only effective therapists available.[6]

In the conventional world actual success seems to be no substitute for "normal professional or scientific training," however ineffective this may be. Six credits of "How to Cure" can carry more weight than actual curing, as in some places two years of teaching in the Peace Corps does not satisfy the requirement for courses in how to teach. I could list dozens of examples of this confusion between the sign and the reality signified, the map and the territory, the medal and the hero, the college degree and the educated person. The literature of General Semantics is full of them. Think how easy it is to get a grade of A in a course on marriage and how difficult it is to achieve a good marriage, as Trainer has pointed out.

In the realm of science there are also plenty of situations of this sort in which experiential knowledge counts for much or is even *sine qua non,* fields in which mere spectator knowledge is helpful only when it is added to experiential knowledge rather than substituted for it.

What we approach in the Synanon story is the ultimate absurdity of bureaucratic science, in which some portions of the truth may have to be defined as "unscientific," in which truth is really true only when gathered by properly certified and uniformed "truth collectors" and according to traditionally sanctified methods or ceremonies.[7]

[6] There are many such situations. Drug and alcohol addiction are two better-known examples. But it is also being discovered that Negroes had better deal with Negroes in many situations, Indians with Indians, Jews with Jews, and Catholics with Catholics. The generalization can be pushed far, although sometimes it gets more and more diluted in the process, e.g., women with women, orphans with orphans, spastics with spastics, homosexuals with homosexuals, etc.

[7] Is the diplomate, the Ph.D., the M.D., the professional, the only person permitted to be wise? knowledgeable? insightful? to discover? to cure? Must there be a laying on of hands by some bishop before one is permitted to enter the holy of holies? to forgive sins? Is it really wise and functional to demand a college degree as a prerequisite for so many jobs rather than seeking actual education, knowledge, skill, capacity, suitability for the job?

KNOWLEDGE WHICH BLINDS

We can view this set of problems from still another angle, which I can illustrate with the Maslow Art Test, something my wife and I made up to test for holistic perception and intuition by testing the ability to detect the style of an artist (55, 57). One of our discoveries was that "knowledge of art," as in art majors, professional artists, etc., sometimes helped and sometimes hurt performance in this test. The better way to perceive "style" is not to analyze or dissect it but to be receptive, global, intuitive. For instance, so far there is some evidence to indicate that a quick reaction is apt to be more successful (57) than long, careful, meticulous study.

This prerequisite for holistic perception of qualities of wholeness I shall call "experiential naïveté," and I define it as a willingness and an ability to experience immediately without certain other ways of "knowing." It means setting aside all our tendencies to rubricize, to know instead of to perceive, to dissect into elements, to split apart. After all, a quality of wholeness is something which pervades the whole and is lost by dissecting.

So those individuals who "know" art only in the analytic,

---

Is a classroom really the only place or the best place to get educated? Is all knowledge conveyable in words? Can it all be put into books? into courses of lectures? Can it always be measured by written tests? Must *any* mother defer to *any* child psychologist? Are ministers in charge of all religious experiences? Must one take courses in "Introduction to Creative Writing," "Intermediate Creative Writing," and "Advanced Creative Writing" before writing a poem? Will a living room chosen by an expert, certified, and professional interior decorator make me happier than my own choice? These questions deliberately push to the extreme. Only so long as we remain watchful and suspicious of the dangers of bureaucratizing, of politically structured organizations, and of churches may we soberly acknowledge their necessity. And only if we remember how easily a technologist can become a means specialist, forgetting about ends, can we use him well and avoid the dangers of "rule by experts."

Someone has defined technology as "the knack of so arranging the world that we don't have to experience it."

atomistic, taxonomic, or historical sense are less able to perceive and enjoy. And the possibility must be admitted that education of a merely analytic sort may actually diminish originally present intuitiveness. (A better example might be conventional mathematics "education," which is far more successful in teaching children to be blind to the beauties and wonders of mathematics.) In every field of knowledge, there exist some "blind knowers" of this sort—botanists who are blind to the beauty of flowers, child psychologists who make children flee in terror, librarians who hate their books to be taken out, literary critics who condescend to poets, the dried-out teacher who ruins his subject for his students, etc. There are the Ph.D.'s who are "licensed fools" and the joyless non-scholars who publish only to avoid perishing, the ones of whom one girl whispered to another at a party, "He's no fun; he doesn't know anything but facts."

Some artists, some poets, some "hysterical" people who rely heavily on feeling, emotion, intuition, and impulsiveness, some religious people, the more mystical people are apt to stop right there. They may then repudiate knowledge, education, science, and intellect as destroyers of instinctive feeling, of innate intuition, of natural piety, of innocent perspicuity. I think this strain of anti-intellectual suspicion runs far deeper than we realize, even in intellectuals themselves. For instance, I think it is one of the sources of the deeper misunderstandings between women and men in our culture. And recent history has shown how it can erupt into terrible political philosophies.

Orthodox, analytic, mechanistic science has no really good way of defending itself against these charges because there is a fair amount of truth and justice in them. A more inclusive conception of science *can*, however, meet and answer these accusations, i.e., a science that includes the idiographic, the experiential, the Taoistic, the comprehensive, the holistic, the personal, the transcendent, the final, etc.

Our art test can serve us as an instance. Assuming that more careful research will confirm our strong first impressions, then it seems also to be true that there are other people whose perspicuity, intuitiveness, and ability to perceive style are improved and enriched by education and by knowledge. Somehow they are able to bring nomothetic, abstract, lawful, verbal knowledge to bear upon their experiencing of the individual instance. Their knowledge helps them to perceive and makes their perceiving richer, more complex, and more enjoyable. In the extreme instance it can enhance even the transcendent aspects of reality, the sacred, the mysterious, the miraculous, the awe-inspiring, the final. Even saintliness, that was supposed by many to come only with naïveté and innocence, we are now finding may come rather with sophistication and knowledge, at least with the kind of more inclusive knowledge that I am talking about. (This observation or hypothesis or guess is an extrapolation from my studies of self-actualizing people and of the effects of psychotherapy rather than from the art test.)

It is just these people, the sages, in whom wisdom, goodness, perspicuity, and learning become a unity, who manage somehow to retain this "experiential naïveté," this "creative attitude" (45), this ability to see freshly as a child sees, without a priori expectations or demands, without knowing in advance what they will see. I have tried to understand how and why this happens (45, 47), but the ability to transform abstract knowledge into richer experiencing is still a mystery and is therefore most obviously a rich question for research. The broader research questions are: when does knowledge conceal and when does it reveal?

### "PROOF" OF EXPERIENCE

What can the word "proof" mean in the experiential realm? How can I prove to someone that I am experiencing vividly, that, for example, I am profoundly moved? And how can this be "validated" in the usual external sense of this term? Of course it is valid to me if I am authentically and vividly experiencing it. But how to prove this to someone else? Is there some shared external thing that we can both point to simultaneously? How describe it, communicate it, measure it, verbalize it?

There are special difficulties here. Many people have called experience ineffable, incommunicable, unverbalizable, impossible for scientists to work with. But often these difficulties are consequences more of the world of abstraction than of the world of experience. Communications of a kind and of a degree are possible, but they are of a kind different from that which exists between chemists (see *48,* app. F on "rhapsodic communication," *43,* app.). Abstract, verbal, unambiguous communication may be less effective for some purposes than metaphorical, poetic, esthetic, primary process techniques.

# 7

# Abstracting and Theorizing

Now that I have expounded on the virtues, the necessities and the priority of experiential knowledge to abstract knowledge, I turn to the virtues and beauties and necessities of abstract knowledge as well. By now my general point must be clear. It is the dichotomized, solely abstract knowledge that is so dangerous, the abstractions and the systems that are opposed to or dichotomized from experience instead of being built upon it and integrated with it. If I may say it so, abstract knowledge dichotomized from experiential knowledge is false and dangerous; but abstract knowledge built upon and hierarchically-integrated with experiential knowledge is a necessity for human life.

Abstractness begins with all orderings of experience, all interpretations of it, and all the hierarchical and Gestaltlike arrangements of experiential knowledge that make it possible for the limited human being to encompass it, grasp it, not be overwhelmed by it. In the same way that our immediate memory span for separate objects is about seven or eight or so, it is also known that six or seven or eight groups of separate objects may also be perceived and encompassed in an immediate perception. This is the simplest example of the holistic hierarchizing of many objects that I can think of. Make these groupings more and more inclusive, and finally it is possible for a human being, limited though he is, to encompass the whole world in a single unified perception. The contrast is with total anarchy, total chaos, a total lack of ordering, or clustering, or of relationships among all these separate things. This is the world, perhaps, of the newborn baby in some respects, or like the world of the panicky schizophrenic in another respect. In any case, it is hardly possible to live with for any length of time or to endure (although it can be enjoyed for a short time). This is even more true if we take into account the necessity for pragmatic living within the world, surviving in it, dealing with it, and having commerce with it. All the means-end relationships, and all the differential perception of ends and means also come under the head of abstractness. Purely concrete experience does not differentiate one experience from another experience in any way, certainly not in terms of relative importance or of relative hierarchy of means and ends. All classifications of our experiences of reality are abstractions, and so is all awareness of similarities and differences.

In other words, abstractness is absolutely necessary for life itself. It is also necessary for the fullest and highest development of human nature. Self-actualization necessarily implies abstractness. It is not even possible to conceive of human self-actualization without whole systems of symbols, abstractions, and words, i.e., language, philosophy, world view.

The attack upon abstractness dichotomized from concreteness must never be confused with an attack upon abstractness hierarchically-integrated with concreteness and experience. We might remind ourselves here of the contemporary situation in philosophy. Kierkegaard and Nietzsche, to take two major examples, attacked not philosophy in general but the great abstract systems of philosophy that had long since cut themselves off from their foundations in actual living experience. Existentialism and phenomenology are in large part also a repudiation of these huge, verbal, a priori, abstract, total systems of philosophy. This is an attempt to get back to life iself, that is to say, to concrete experience upon which all abstractions must be based if they are to remain alive.

It will help here to make the distinction between an empirical generalization or theory and an a priori generalization or theory. The former is simply an effort to organize and to unify experiential knowledge so that we can grasp it with our limited human brain. An a priori theory makes no such effort. It can be spun entirely inside one's own head and can proceed without reference either to experiential knowledge or to areas of ignorance. Generally it is presented as a certainty. In effect it commits the great sin of denying human ignorance. The true empiricist or the empirical-minded layman is always aware of what he knows and what he doesn't know and of the relative reliabilities and different levels of validity of what he does know. An empirical theory is in a real sense humble. The classical, abstract, a priori theory need not be humble; it can be and often is arrogant. One might also say that the abstract theory or abstract system becomes functionally autonomous in the sense of divorcing itself from its empirical foundations, from the experiences upon which it rests and which it is supposed to explain or give meaning to or organize. It proceeds thereafter to live its own life as a theory per se, sufficient unto itself, having its own life. In contrast the empirical theory or empirical system remains connected with the experiential facts that it organizes into a manageable, graspable unity and in close parallel with these facts. As a consequence it can shift and change and easily modify itself as new information becomes available. That is, if it purports to interpret and organize our knowledge of reality, then it must of necessity be a changing thing, since our knowledge of reality keeps on changing, and it must be adaptable and flexible in the sense of adapting itself to this foundation of changing and increasing knowledge. There is a kind of mutual feedback involved here between theory and facts, a feedback which can be totally lacking in the functionally autonomous abstract theory or system which has become self-borne.

To add a final touch to this differentiation, I refer to a previously made distinction between reduction to the concrete as Goldstein described it (22) and reduction to the abstract as I described it (47). I will then contrast both of these with the finding in self-actualizing people that characteristically they were able to be both concrete and abstract.

I can push the whole matter even further. In a certain sense I see the acceptance of the prepotency and the logical priority of experience as another version of the spirit of empiricism itself. One of the beginnings of science, one of the roots from which it grew, was the determination not to take things on faith, trust, logic, or authority but to check and to see for oneself. Experience had shown how often the logic or the a priori certainty or Aristotle's authority failed to work in fact. The lesson was easy to draw. First, before everything else comes the seeing of nature with your own eyes, that is, experiencing it yourself.

Perhaps an even better example is the development of the empirical or the scientific attitude in the child. Here the major injunction is "let's take a look for ourselves," or "go and see with your own eyes." For the child this contrasts with taking things on faith, whether from daddy or mommy or from the teacher or from the book. It can be phrased in the harshest terms of "don't trust anyone, but look with your own eyes." Or else it can be phrased more mildly: "it's always a good idea to check just to make sure. There are individual differences in perceiving; somebody else might see it in one way, and you perhaps will see it in another." This is to teach the child that one's own perceptions usually constitute the court of last resort. If the empirical attitude means anything at all, it means at least this. First comes "knowing" in the experiential sense; then come the checks on the fallibilities of the senses and of experiential knowledge; then come the abstractions, the theories, i.e., orthodox science. As a matter of fact, the concept of objectivity itself (in the sense of the need to make knowledge public and to share it and not to trust it completely until it has been shared by at least several people) may be seen as a more complex derivative of a primary empirical rule, i.e., to check by one's own experience. This is so because public knowledge constitutes an experiential check by several people on your report of your private experience. If you go into the desert and discover some unexpected mine or some improbable animal, your experiential knowledge may be certain and valid, but you can hardly expect others to believe you entirely and on faith. They also have a right to see for themselves, that is, to acquire the ultimate validity of their own experiential knowledge. And that is just what objective public checking is, i.e., an extension of "see for yourself."

This insistence upon the priority of the empirical theory over the a priori theory or system and the consequent insistence upon a close parallelism of the empirical theory with the facts that it ties together in a unity, differentiates between the person with the empirical attitude on the one hand and the doctrinaire on the other. For instance, Max Eastman in his autobiography thinks of himself, by contrast with the Soviet intellectuals, as a "vulgar empiricist who saw Socialism as a hypothesis, an experiment that ought to be tried." He was restless with the Soviet theorists, among whom he felt "an atmosphere of theology rather than of science." I have criticized the religious establishments on a similar basis (48). Since most of them have claimed to be revealed religions, that is, to be based upon an original prophets' vision of the perfect, final, and absolute truth, there is obviously nothing more to learn. There is no need for openness, for checking, for experimentation, not even for improvement (since it is already perfect).

This is as sharp a contrast with the empirical attitude as I can find. But in a milder form it is widespread and perhaps we could say almost universal in the mass of humankind. And I am not even inclined to exempt all professional scientists from this indictment. The empirical attitude is in its essence a humble attitude, and many or most scientists are not humble except in their own chosen areas of professional work. They are, many of them, as likely to charge out of their laboratory doors with a priori faiths and prejudgments of all kinds as are some theologians, if only about the nature of science itself. This humility that I consider to be a defining characteristic of the empirical or scientific attitude includes the ability to admit that you are ignorant and that mankind in general is ignorant about many things. Such an admission has the necessary consequence of making you in principle willing and eager to learn. It means that you are open rather than closed to new data. It means that you can be naïve rather than all-knowing. And all of this means, of course, that your universe keeps on growing steadily in contrast to the static universe of the person who already knows everything.

This is a long way off from the point at which I started, that is, of simply insisting on a place in knowledge and in science for experiential data. But I believe that making a respectable place for experiential data finally strengthens the empirical attitude and therefore strengthens science rather than weakens it. It expands the jurisdiction of science because of its faith that the human mind need not be shut out of any area of life.

# 8

## Comprehensive Science and Simpleward Science

The inclusion of subjective experiences in the world of reality knowable by the scientist (for us now defined as wanting to know all of reality, not just the shared, public portions of it) breeds two consequences at least. One is the obvious differentiation between the immediacy of experiential knowledge and the distance of what I have called "spectator knowledge." The other is the notion that scientific work has two directions or poles or goals: one is toward utter simplicity and condensation, the other toward total comprehensiveness and inclusiveness.

If there is any primary rule of science, it is, in my opinion, acceptance of the obligation to acknowledge and describe all of reality, all that exists, everything that is the case. Before all else science must be comprehensive and all-inclusive. It must accept within its jurisdiction even that which it cannot understand or explain, that for which no theory exists, that which cannot be measured, predicted, controlled, or ordered. It must accept even contradictions and illogicalities and mysteries, the vague, the ambiguous, the archaic, the unconscious, and all other aspects of existence that are difficult to communicate. At its best it is completely open and excludes nothing. It has no "entrance requirements."

Furthermore it includes all levels or stages of knowledge, including the inchoate. Knowledge has an embryology, too; it cannot confine itself to its final and adult forms alone. Knowledge of low reliability is also part of knowledge. At this point, however, my main intention is to include subjective experiences in this all-inclusive realm of being and then to pursue some of the radical consequences of this inclusion.

Such knowledge is of course apt to be less reliable, less communicable, less measurable, etc. And of course one push of science is toward the more public, toward the more "objective." In that direction lies the shared certainty that we all seek and enjoy. And ordinarily this is ultimately the direction in which technological progress is most likely. If I could only discover some external indicator of, for example, happiness or anxiety, some litmus paper test of the subjective, I would be a very happy man. But happiness and anxiety now exist even in the absence of such objective tests. It is the denial of this existence that I consider so silly that I won't bother arguing about it. Anyone who tells me that my emotions or desires don't exist is in effect, telling me that *I* don't exist.

Once the break has been made and experiential data have been acknowledged as part of knowledge and therefore of science (comprehensively defined), we are confronted with many real problems, difficulties, and paradoxes. For one thing, it seems that we must begin, philosophically and scientifically, with experience. For each of us it is precisely some of his subjective experiences that are the most certain, the most undoubted, the least questionable of all data. Especially is this true if I am a schizophrenic. Then my subjective experiences may become the only reliable reality. But just as the schizophrenic is not content with his subjective world alone and makes desperate efforts to reach the reality outside and to cling to it, so do we all seek to know and to live in the extra-psychic world of "reality," almost from birth on. We *need* to know it at all the levels of meaning of the word "know." The intrapsychic world, much of it, is too fluctuating, too changeable. It doesn't stay put. Too often we don't know what to expect of it. And it is obviously influenced by happenings "outside" of it.

Not only the world of nature but also the social world of people beckon us out of our private inner worlds. From our beginnings we cling to the mother as she clings to us, and here too an outside-the-ego kind of reality starts forming. In such ways we begin to make the differentiation between our subjective experiences that we share with others and those which we discover to be peculiarly our own. And it is this world that correlates with the shared experiences that we finally learn to call external reality, a world of happenings and things that you and I can point to, i.e., that produce similar experiences in you and me at the same time. In various senses this external world is discovered to be independent of our wishes and fears, our attention to it, etc.

Science or knowledge in sum total can be considered a codification, a purification, a structuring and organizing of all these shared experiences. It has been a way of enabling us to grasp them and to make them comprehensible by unifying and simplifying them. This monistic trend, this pressure toward simplicity and parsimony, this yearning to make a single inclusive formula out of a lot of little ones, has come to be identified with science and with knowledge.

For most people the far goal of science, its end and therefore its ideal and defining essence, still is its comprehensive "laws," elegant and "simple" mathematical formulas, pure and abstract concepts and models, ultimate and irreducible elements and variables. And so for these people these ultimate abstractions have become the most real reality. Reality lies *behind* the appearances and is inferred rather than perceived.

The blueprints are more real than the houses. The maps are more real than the territory.

What I propose here is that this is only one direction in which science can develop, one limit toward which it yearns to approach. Another direction is toward comprehensiveness, allness, and the acceptance of all concrete experience, all suchness, all esthetic savoring of the full richness of everything without needing to abstract. I would equally avoid reduction to the concrete or reduction to the abstract.[1] I would remind you again that any abstraction loses something of concrete, experiential reality. And with equal emphasis I would remind you that the abstractions are necessary if we are to avoid total insanity and if we wish to live in the world. The solution of this dilemma that I have worked out for myself and that works well for me is to know when I am abstracting and when I am concretizing, to be able to do both, to enjoy them both, and to know the values and shortcomings of both. With Whitehead, we can then "seek simplicity and distrust it."

Accepting experiential data as scientific data creates problems. But also many problems disappear if we accept both worlds. On the one hand we have the traditional scientific world, unifying and organizing multiplex experience, moving toward simplicity, economy, parsimony, succinctness, and

---

[1] ". . . Science should resolutely set its face against anything which would limit its scope, or which would arbitrarily narrow the methods or perspectives of its own pursuit of knowledge.

"Valuable as have been the contributions of behaviorism, I believe that time will indicate the unfortunate effects of the bounds it has tended to impose. To limit oneself to consideration of externally observable behaviors, to rule out consideration of the whole universe of inner meanings, of purposes, of the inner flow of experiencing, seems to me to be closing our eyes to great areas which confront us when we look at the human world. . . .

"In contrast, the trend of which I am speaking will attempt to face up to *all* of the realities in the psychological realm. Instead of being restrictive and inhibiting, it will throw open the whole range of human experiencing to scientific study" (*65*, 80).

unity. On the other hand we accept also the world of subjective experiences, affirming that these too exist, that they are part of reality, that they are worthy of our interest, and that there is even some possibility of understanding and organizing them (quite apart from the primary rule of science—to accept what exists as real, i.e., not to deny any reality, even if we cannot understand it or explain it or communicate it).

Science, then, has two directions or tasks, not just one. It moves toward abstractness (unity, parsimony, economy, simplicity, integration, lawfulness, "graspability"). But it also moves toward comprehensiveness, toward experiencing everything, toward describing all these experiences, toward accepting all that exists. Thus we may speak about the two kinds of reality that many have spoken of, for instance Northrop (58).[2] The world of experience exists and comprehends all experiences, i.e., the experiential, phenomenological, or esthetically experienced world. The other, the world of the physicists, mathematicians, and chemists, of abstractions, "laws," and formulas, of systems of postulates, is a world that is not directly experienced but rather rests *upon* the experiential world, is inferred from it, and is an effort to comprehend it and to make sense of it, to see behind its contradictions, to order it and structure it.

Is the abstract world of the physicist more "real" than the world of the phenomenologist? Why need we think so? If anything the contradiction of this statement is easier to defend.

[2] Collating from various of Northrop's writings, we have the two sets of phrases to describe the two kinds of knowledge or of reality. On the one hand, Concepts of Postulation: the theoretic component of things, the theoretic continuum, the theoretically known, the scientifically known, the inferred, the theoretically inferred, inferred facts. Contrasted with these are Concepts by Inspection or by Intuition: the esthetic component of things, the esthetic continuum, the ineffable, the purely factually given, transitory sense data, the empirically known, impressionistically known, immediately apprehended, empirically immediate, pure fact, purely empirical, immediately experienced, pure observation, the sensuous qualities.

What exists here and now and what we actually experience is certainly more immediately real than the formula, the symbol, the sign, the blueprint, the word, the name, the schema, the model, the equation, etc. What exists now is in this same sense more real than its origins, its putative constituents or causes or precursors; it is experientially more real than anything it can be reduced to. At the very least we must reject the definition of reality as being *only* the abstractions of science.

## EMPIRICAL AND ABSTRACT THEORIES

This continuum from comprehensiveness to simplicity can help us to understand better the important difference between "empirical theories" and "constructed" or "abstract theories." The former are more an expression of science's effort to be comprehensive (at the same time that it organizes and classifies multiplicity in order to make it more graspable by the limited human being). It is essentially an effort to order the facts rather than to explain them. The Linnaean system is the classical example. The original Freudian system is another such "empirical theory," in my opinion. It seems to me to be primarily a taxonomy, one might say almost a filing system in which all the clinical discoveries can find a place.

The abstract (or constructed) system is determined far more by its system properties than by its loyalty to the facts, as the empirical theory is. In principle it need have nothing to do with facts; it can be an arbitrary construction, e.g., the non-Euclidean geometries. A good theory in this sense is primarily like a good mathematician's demonstration. It is as succinct as possible, moving ideally toward a single equation. It is like a good system of logic, obeying its own given rules. It may or may not be "useful" but need not be. This kind of "pure" theory has often come before the fact, like a suit of clothes playfully designed for some fantasied, nonexistent species that later may have turned out to be useful for some other, unforeseen purpose; or like a chemical newly synthesized for its own sake, for which uses are subsequently sought and perhaps found ("I have discovered a cure; but for what disease?").

A good empirical theory may be a sloppy abstract theory, self-contradictory, complicated, incoherent, with overlapping categories (rather than mutually exclusive ones), with unclear and equivocal definitions. Its first loyalty is to include all the facts somewhere within its jurisdiction, even if this makes for sloppiness.

A good abstract theory stresses rather the simplifying and neatening function of science.

In other words, we see exemplified also here in the realm of theory-making the twofold task of science. On the one hand it must describe and accept the "way things are," the actual world as it is, understandable or not, meaningful or not, explainable or not. Facts must come before theories. On the other hand it also presses steadily toward simplicity, unity, and elegance, toward condensed, succinct, and abstract formulas for describing the essence of reality, its skeletal structure, the ultimate to which it can be reduced.[3] Ultimately the good theory does both, or at least tries to. Or more accurately said, the good *theorist* does both and gets satisfactions from both kinds of success, especially if both can come simultaneously.

Any scientific theory has not only system properties, which are the characteristics of a "good theory," but also empirical determinants. That is, it tries not only to be a good theory but also to be true as a description and organization of what exists. It is faithful to the nature of reality and tries to make it more graspable, essentially by simplifying and abstracting.

If this twofold nature of any scientific theory were fully

---

[3] Toward maps, graphs, formulas, schemata, equations, diagrams, blueprints, abstract art, X-rays, outlines, condensations, précis, summaries, symbols, signs, cartoons, sketches, models, skeletons, plans, charts, recipes.

accepted, we should have far less trouble with crude empirical theories like psychoanalysis. The Freudian system is primarily a description of many experiences. It is far from being a "formal" or elegant theory. But the fact that it is not "formal" or "hypothetico-deductive" is distinctly secondary to the fact that it describes systematically and correctly a multitude of clinical experiences. First one should ask how accurate and how true to experience it is rather than how elegant and how abstracted it is. Most qualified people—that is, with the proper kind of experience and training—would agree, I think, that Freud's set of clinical descriptions is mostly veridical, i.e., that his collection of "facts" is largely true. This is so even though certain of his specific efforts at grand theorizing and at constructing a "system" can be argued with or rejected.

A scientist's first duty, then, is to describe the facts. If these conflict with the demand for a "good system," then out with the system. Systematizing and theorizing come after the facts. Or, to avoid ruminating over what a fact is, let us say that the first task of the scientist is to experience truly that which exists. It is amazing how often this truism gets lost.

## SYSTEM PROPERTIES

Much confusion in the world of science could be bypassed by realizing that "system properties," i.e., the properties that inhere in theoretical, abstract structures of thought, apply only to the simplifying direction of scientific thought. They do not apply to the world of comprehensive experience, in which the only scientific requirement is to accept what exists. Whether experience is meaningful or not, mysterious or not, illogical or contradictory simply does not matter in the realm of experience. Nor is it required that experience be structured, organized, measured, weighed, or aligned in any way to other experiences. The ideal pole here is the innocent and fully concentrated experiencing of the suchness of the experience. Any other process or activity can only detract from the full reality of the experience and therefore constitutes a kind of interference with the perception of this kind of truth.

The ideal model of a theoretical or abstract system is a mathematical or logical system like Euclid's geometry, or better for our purposes, the Lobachevski geometry or one of the other non-Euclidean geometries because they are more independent of reality, i.e., of nonsystem determinants. Here apart from truth, reality, or veridicality we can talk about a theory being a "good" theory because it is internally consistent, it covers everything, it is parsimonious, economical, condensed, and "elegant." The more abstract it is, the better theory it is. Each variable or separable aspect of the theory has a name and just this name, and nothing else has this name. Furthermore it is definable. One can say exactly what it is and what it is not. Its perfection consists in the most fully abstracted inclusion of everything in the system in a single mathematical formula. Each statement or formula or equation has a single meaning and can have no other (unlike a figure of speech or a painting), and it conveys this and only this same meaning to each onlooker. The good theory is obviously a generalization. That is, it is a way of classifying, organizing, structuring, simplifying huge numbers of separate instances, even infinite numbers of them. It does not refer to any one experience or to any one thing or object but to categories or kinds of things or experiences.

This can be a game in itself and has been used often enough precisely as an intellectual exercise having nothing whatsoever to do with reality. One could manufacture a theory to cover some class of objects or happenings or some imaginary world, starting with completely arbitrary definitions, going on to completely arbitrary operations, and then playing the game of generating deductions from them. It is in this kind of system that many of our "scientific" words and concepts belong. "Definition" and especially "exact or rigorous definition" is of the world of abstractions, i.e., it is a system property. It is completely irrelevant to experienced suchness. It just doesn't apply. An experience of redness or of pain is its own definition, i.e., its own felt quality or suchness. It is what it is. It is itself. So ultimately is any process of classifying that is always a reference to something beyond the suchness of an experience. Indeed, this holds true for any abstracting process whatsoever, which by definition is a cutting into the suchness of an experience, taking part of it and throwing the rest away. In contrast the fullest savoring of an experience discards nothing but takes it all in.

So for the concepts "law" and "order"—these, too, are system properties, as are also "prediction" and "control." Any "reduction" is a happening within a theoretical system.

### EXPERIENCING AND RUBRICIZING

Long ago I learned from my artist-wife of her irritation with some of my scientist's obsessional classifying ways. For example, I asked always, in a kind of conversational tic, for the name of the bird or the flower or the tree that I admired. It was as if I were not content to admire and to enjoy but also had to do something intellectual about it. And often that "something intellectual" substituted for or displaced altogether the drinking in and contemplative enjoyment of "the way things are." This process of classifying in lieu of real perceiving and experiencing I call "rubricizing" (*38*), which means the pathologizing of the "normal" or "healthy" effort to organize and unify a truly experienced world.

The reader may perhaps profit from my mistakes. I saw myself sometimes "rubricizing" in the art gallery as well, looking first at the name plate rather than the painting, and again not really perceiving but rather classifying, e.g., "Oh yes! a Renoir, quite typical, nothing unusual or startling, easily recognizable, nothing to attract attention, no need to study it (since I already "know" it), no novelty here, what's next?" And once, when I looked first at a most beautiful drawing— *really* looked and really enjoyed—I was startled to find out later that it was by Gainsborough—of all unfashionable people! I think that had I first looked at the name, I might not have really seen the drawing because of the a priori classification and filing system I carried in my head and in which I had already decided that Gainsborough gave me no pleasure and wasn't worth looking at.

I learned also, in a well-remembered illumination, that a robin or a bluejay is a most beautiful and miraculous thing, as all birds are. Even common ones are just as beautiful as the rare birds. The judgment of commonness is outside the experience itself and has nothing to do with its own nature. Such a judgment can be a way of dismissing the experience, a way of not paying attention to it. That is, it can be a way of blinding ourselves. Any sunset or oak tree or baby or pretty girl is a fantastic and unbelievable, unassimilable miracle if seen for the first time, or if seen *as if* for the first time (or as if for the *last* time), as a good artist sees or as any good experiencer sees. This fresh and defamiliarized experiencing becomes easy for any person as soon as he has sense enough to realize that it is more fun to live in a world of miracles than in a world of filing cabinets and that a familiar miracle is still a miracle.

The pertinent (and sententious) moral for both the lay knower and the scientist knower is that not fully experiencing is a form of blindness that no would-be scientist can afford. Not only does this maneuver deprive him of many of the joys of science, but it threatens to make him a poor scientist.

Another blessing that came to me from insight into my rubricizing is that I did not have to oppose "experiencing" to "organizing-integrating" nor the esthetic to the scientific way. I learned that "scientific knowledge" actually enriched my experiencing rather than impoverishing it, if only I didn't use it as a substitute for experiencing. The knowledgeable experiencer can often be a better enjoyer than the ignorant experiencer, if we accept the formula "First look, and then know." We can now add to it, "and then look again," and we will see how much better cognizing becomes, how much more enjoyable, how much richer, how much more mysterious and awesome.

Fortunately "real experiencing" is so often enjoyable and even rapturous, if it is holistic enough, i.e., cosmic and mystical enough. It is often "enjoyable" even when it is also painful and sad. At any rate, by comparison with mere rubricizing, it is more often enjoyable. Rubricizing, i.e., shuffling, classifying, and filing the nonexperienced, is a thin and bloodless activity, rarely happy or enjoyable except at a low level in the hierarchy of pleasures. At best it is a kind of "relief" rather than a kind of positive enjoyment. To fall into this mode of "knowing" is, then, not only a way of being blind but also a way of being unhappy.

# 9

## Suchness Meaning and Abstractness Meaning

For my own thinking one important by-product of the foregoing considerations has been the illumination of the concept of "meaning." In general we—the intellectuals, the philosophers, the scientists—have meant by it that it integrates, coordinates, classifies, and organizes the chaos, the multiple, and the meaningless many. It is a gestalting, holistic activity, the creation of a whole. This whole and its parts then have the meaning that the parts did not hitherto have. "Organizing experience into meaningful patterns" implies that experience itself has no meaningfulness, that the organizer creates or imposes or donates the meaning, that this giving of meaning is an active process rather than a receptive one, that it is a gift from the knower to the known.

In other words, "meaningfulness" of this kind is of the realm of classification and abstraction rather than of experience. It is an aspect of economical, simpleward knowledge and science rather than of all-descriptive and comprehensive knowledge and science. Frequently I sense also the implication that it is "human-created," i.e., that much of it would vanish if human beings disappeared. And this in turn leads me to align "manmade meaningfulness" with the underlying implication that things (reality, nature, cosmos), having no inherent, intrinsic meaningfulness, must be clothed with meaningfulness, and if man is incapable of doing this, then some god must.

It is possible to counter this ultimately mechanistic world view in two different ways. One is to do as many contemporary artists, composers, screen writers, poets, dramatists, and novelists (and some philosophers, too) have done, and that is to embrace this notion overenthusiastically after being repelled and depressed by it, and to talk about the ultimate absurdity and meaninglessness of life, to paint, write, or compose by chance, to break up meaningfulness as if it could be *only* cliché, to talk of "indeterminacy and the arbitrariness of any human decision," etc.[1] For them meaningfulness is ultimately by fiat and is an arbitrary decision that emerges from no principle, from no requirements, and that is an unpredictable and occasionalistic act of will. Life becomes a series of "happenings," meaningless in itself and without intrinsic values. Such a person can easily become the total skeptic, nihilistic, relativistic, impulsive, without any right or wrong or better or worse. In a word, he becomes a person without values. If the juices of life do not flow strongly within his veins, he will wind up talking about despair, anguish, and suicide. This is as if to say, "O.K.! I must accept it. Life has no meaning. I

[1] When an interviewer confessed to Alain Robbe-Grillet, author of the screenplay "Last Year at Marienbad," an incomplete understanding of the movie, the writer laughed and said, "Moi non plus." This is certainly not an uncommon reaction any more. Sometimes, I feel, it is an "in" thing to do, even a point of pride, to confess to lack of conscious meaningfulness in one's own artistic products and even to imply that the question itself is old-fashioned. This deliberate effort to renounce or to destroy meaningfulness sometimes appears to symbolize destruction of the establishment, of authority, and of traditions and conventions (whose falsehood seems to be taken for granted). Consciously or unconsciously it is intended as an attack upon hypocrisy, as a blow for freedom, for authenticity. It is as if a lie were being destroyed. This kind of obvious dichotomizing gives way easily before hierarchical-integrative attitudes.

must rely entirely on my own arbitrary decisions. I mustn't believe anything or believe *in* anything other than these blind wishes, whims, and impulses for which there is no possible justification outside of their own felt pushiness." Of course this is the most extreme version that I have seen of this attitude, but it is a logical consequence of it.

But this development can be seen in another way altogether, as part of the *Zeitgeist,* as one aspect of the century-long revolt against the great abstract "systems" of religion, economics, philosophy, politics, and even science, which had become so distant from real human needs and experiences that they looked like—and often were—vast hypocrisies and rationalizations. It can be seen as an expression of Dostoevsky's and Nietzsche's dictum that "if God is dead, then anything is permissible." It can be seen from another angle as one consequence of the collapse of all the traditional, extrahuman value systems, which left only one place to turn—into the self and back to experience. It is a kind of testimony to our need for meaning and our despair when we think there is none.

In a positive sense we can call it the return to the sheer experience, which is the beginning of all thought and to which we always return when the abstractions and systems fail us. We then realize more fully that the ultimate meaning of many facts is simply the sheer being of their own existence. Throughout human history many who were forced to doubt have tried to become naïve again, to go back to the beginnings, to think everything through again on a solider and more certain foundation, to ask in a time of turmoil if there were anything that they could be really sure of. There are times in life when patching up and improving seems like a hopeless task and when it is easier to raze the structure altogether and to build again from the ground up.

If we add to this the common human temptation to dichotomize, to choose one side or the other—and therefore to choose either experiential suchness (renouncing all abstraction as the intrinsic enemy) or abstractness, lawfulness, and integrations (renouncing suchness as the enemy of lawfulness)—then these extreme positions can be seen as the pathological consequences of dichotomozing. They can be seen as foolish and unnecessary, even as consequences of the childish inability to be integrative and inclusive (1,2) or to be synergic (49,51).

As we have already seen, it is easily possible to accept and to enjoy the virtues both of suchness and of abstraction. As a matter of fact, it is even necessary for full sanity and humanness to be comfortable with both. I therefore propose to speak of two different kinds of meanings, which are complementary rather than mutually exclusive. I will call the one abstractness meaning and the other suchness meaning, and point out that the one is of the realm of classifications and abstractions and that the other is of the experiential realm. I prefer this usage rather than the equally possible one of saying that the smell of a rose is meaningless or absurd because, for most people, these latter words are still invidious and normative and can therefore lead to pathogenic misunderstandings.

These two kinds of meaningfulness generate two kinds of communication and of expression as well, whether in language, in art, in the cinema, or in poetry. And they even show us again that science has two tasks. One is the full acknowledgment, acceptance, and savoring of concrete, raw experience. The other is the effort to bind these experiences together, to seek out their similarities and differences, to figure out their regularities and their interrelations with each other, to construct them into systems that can be expressed simply and that can thus condense many experiences into a formula (or "law") which comprehends them all and which we can grasp.

But these two tasks or goals are interrelated and cannot be split apart without damage, nor can we choose one to the exclusion of the other, for then we generate a crippled "reduction to the concrete" and a crippled "reduction to the abstract."

## TWO KINDS OF UNDERSTANDABILITY AND EXPLANATION

These two approaches to meaning further clarify such words as "understanding," "predicting," and "explaining." The purely "scientific" person uses these words—unwittingly—in a way different from the ideally intuitive type. For the former an increase in understanding usually comes from and is equal to a move toward the simple. It is more monistic, closer toward unity, an economical reduction of complexity and of chaos. "Understanding" and "explanation" lie behind the manifold and the multiplex and help to make it comprehensible. It joins, for example, cabbages and kings in some integrating organization, some unifying connection, instead of just leaving them there, ununified, for noninterfering contemplation.

For such a person "explaining" and "understanding" both have a reductive effect, in the sense of reducing the number of variables that must be grasped and also in the sense that the surface appearance of the manifold is less "real" than the simpler explanatory theory that lies behind the world of appearances. It is a kind of rejection of face value, and it is a way of reducing mystery. In the extreme instance, for him, that which cannot be explained cannot be real or true.

But for the more experiential type of person, there is also another kind of understanding that parallels "suchness meanings." Understanding something then is experiencing that something in its own right and in its own nature. This experiencing, for instance, of a person or of a painting, can grow deeper, richer, more complex and yet can remain *within* the object that one is trying to understand better. And so we can differentiate experiential understanding from the integrative or abstract understanding that is an active move toward simplification, economy and parsimony.

Far from simplifying and condensing the experience and far from moving toward a diagram of it (or an X-ray or a schema or a mathematical description of it), experiential understanding is content to rest there *within* the experience, not going beyond it, savoring it and getting the taste and smell of it in that direct way. This is the kind of understanding that the sculptor has of clay or stone, that the carpenter has of wood, that a mother has of her baby, that a swimmer has of water, or that a husband and wife have of each other. And this is the kind of understanding that is ultimately impossible for the nonsculptor, the noncarpenter, the nonmother, the nonswimmer, or the nonmarried, no matter what other resources of knowledge may be available.

The word "explanation" as used by scientists normally has *only* a simpleward meaning. It seems always to point beyond the experience, and to represent a theory *about* it. But some artists and critics use the word also in an experiential, self-referential way. This has some usefulness, and at the least we ought to be aware of it. This is the sense in which something experienced is its own explanation. What is the meaning of a leaf, a fugue, a sunset, a flower, a person? They "mean" themselves, explain themselves, and prove themselves. Many modern painters or musicians and even poets reject the now old-fashioned demand that works of art "mean" something beyond themselves, that they point outward and have nonself reference, or that they have a message, or that they be "explainable" in the ordinary scientific sense of simplification. They are rather self-contained worlds that are to be looked *at* rather than through. They are not a step to something else, nor are they stations on the road to some other terminus. They are not signs or symbols standing for something other than

themselves. Neither can they be "defined" in the ordinary
sense of being placed within a class or in a historical sequence
or in some other relationship to the world outside themselves.
Most musicians, many painters, and even some poets will
refuse even to talk about their works or to "interpret" them
beyond labeling them in some purely arbitrary way or merely
pointing at them and saying, "Look!" or "Listen!"[2]

And yet even in this realm of discourse people *do* talk of
studying a Beethoven quartet (in the experiential sense of
immersing oneself *in* it, of repeated exposure and contemplation, of minute examination of its inner structure under a
higher power of the microscope, so to speak, rather than of
studying *about* it). And then they say that they understand it
more profoundly. There is a school of literary criticism with
similar tenets, whose adherents rely on close examination of
the work itself rather than upon its sociological, historical,
political, or economic context. These people have not relapsed
into the silence that ineffability would seem to call for. They
have much to say, and they *do* use the words "meaning,"
"explanation," "understanding," "interpretation," and "communication," although of course still trying to stay strictly
within the experience.

In my opinion these positive usages from the world of art
are helpful in a reconstructed philosophy of science that includes rather than excludes experiential data. I think they are
preferable to the other style of usage that talks of "meaninglessness" and "absurdity" rather than of "suchness meaning",
that reduces itself to pointing rather than to verbal communi-

[2] T. S. Eliot, when asked, "Please, Sir, what do you mean by the line:
'Lady, three white leopards sat under a juniper tree'?" replied: "I mean,
'Lady, three white leopards sat under a juniper tree' . . . " (Stephen Spender,
"Remembering Eliot," *Encounter*, XXIV [April 1965], 4). Picasso has been
similarly quoted: "Everyone wants to understand art. Why not try to understand the song of a bird? Why does one love the night, flowers, everything
around one, without trying to understand it? But in the case of a painting
people have to understand."

cation, that repudiates any effort to explain or to define, and that can only wait for the illumination to happen without being able in any way to help it come, saying, in effect, "If you don't get it, you never will."

The positive usage promises, I think, more sophisticated and insightful commerce with experiential data and more pragmatic and fruitful management of them. The words "absurd," "meaningless," "ineffable," and "unexplainable" imply a failure of nerve because they talk of a nothing, a zero, an absence of something rather than a presence that can be dealt with scientifically. The positive usages are also justified by the fact that they imply the acceptance of the possibility that experiences can be end experiences, valid and valuable in themselves. These usages are appropriate to a Psychology of Being, i.e., a psychology that deals with ends and with final states of being. Negative usages imply acceptance of the classical scientific insistence on being value-free and on having nothing to do with ends but only with means to ends (which are somehow arbitrarily given).

### THE SUCHNESS MEANING OF LIFE

Many basic experiences in life, perhaps ultimately all experiences, are "unsolvable." That is to say, they are impossible to understand. You can't make any sense out of them beyond their own is-ness. You can't be rational about them; they just are. About all you can do with them is simply to recognize their existence, to accept them, and, whenever possible, to enjoy them in their richness and mystery, at the same time realizing that they constitute much of the answer to the question "What is the meaning of life?"

Life is in part its own meaning. That is, the sheer experiencing of living, or walking, of seeing, of tastes and smells, of sensuous and emotional experiences, and all the rest help to make life worthwhile. When they are no longer positively enjoyed, life itself is called into question, and we have the possibility of boredom, ennui, depression and suicide. Then we say, "Life is meaningless," or "What's the sense of living," or "Life is no longer worthwhile." It is for this reason also that I prefer to speak in terms of suchness meaning rather than to concede meaninglessness.

### LAWFUL EXPLANATION AND SUCHNESS UNDERSTANDING

The differentiation of suchness meaning from abstractness meaning, of suchness understanding from abstraction understanding, and of suchness explanation from simpleward explanation has taught me something else as well.

About fifteen years ago I began an investigation into the motivations of characterologically different types of scientists. I asked them simply to ramble on at length in answer to my two questions "Why did you pick your line of work, your field, your problem?" and "What are the main rewards (the gratifications, the pleasure, the kicks, the peak moments of highest happiness) that you get out of your work? What keeps you at it? Why do you love your work?" These two questions parallel the difference between "Why did you fall in love?" and "Why do you stay married?"

For various reasons, I had to give up this research after interviewing perhaps a dozen scientists in various fields. But even with these few I became impressed with the variety of covert motives that impelled scientists to their work and kept them at it. As with other human beings, their world view, their pleasures and satisfactions, their likes and dislikes, their vocational choices, and their styles of work were in part an expression of their "characters."

I was confronted again, as so many other investigators have been, with the temptation to differentiate the contrasting types that have been called by so many names, tough-minded and tender-minded, Apollonian and Dionysian, anal and oral, obsessional and hysterical, masculine and feminine, controlled and impulsive, dominating and receptive, suspicious and trusting, etc. For a time I used the designations $x$ character and $y$ character, defining these as the common elements in all these pairs of antonyms. At other times I used the words "cool" and "warm" because neither of these is invidious or insulting, and I thought also that the "physiognomic quality" of these words was better than more explicitly defined words in the present state of knowledge. For the same reasons I have also tried the "blue-green" (end of the spectrum) and contrasted it with "red-orange-yellow" people. Finally I put the problem aside, even though the feeling of being on the edge of some vast illumination even yet lingers. The trouble is that it has remained in this same teasing position for fifteen years, without my getting any closer to illumination.

One impression, tentative at the time, has become more convincing over the years, and I offer it here for more careful testing. Those individuals that I thought of as "cool" or "blue-green" or "tough-minded" in character and outlook tended, it seemed to me, to have as the goals of their scientific work the establishment of law, of regularities, of certainty, of exactness. They spoke of "explanation," and by this they clearly implied the tendency toward parsimony, and economy, the simple, the monistic. The moment of reductiveness, i.e., of a reduction in the number of variables, was a moment of triumph and of high achievement. By contrast I felt that the "warm" people, the red-orange-yellow, the intuitive ones (who come closer to the poet-artist-musician than to the engineer-technologist), the "tender-minded" and "soft-nosed" scientists tended to speak glowingly of the moment of "understanding" as the high spot and the reward of investigation, i.e., suchness understanding. In a word, it looks as if the distribution on the characterological continuum from tough-minded to tender-minded may be paralleled by a continuum with "lawful explanation" at one end and "suchness understanding" at the other.[3]

This comes close to hypothesizing that "abstract knowledge" and "experiential knowledge" are the contrasting goals (for the pure or extreme types).

[3] In the very creative or great scientists I felt that, as is their custom, they integrated both qualities instead of giving up one in favor of the other. Even so I found it useful to make this typological differentiation, and so did some of the people I talked with and some whose personal accounts I have read. The question for them is when to be tough and when soft, rather than which to be—hard or soft. Within psychology, my impression remains that some such polar differentiation may separate those "typical" experimental psychologists (who are poor clinicians) from the "typical" clinical psychologists (who are poor researchers), even though the one small research that I completed does not strongly support this guess (55).

# 10

# Taoistic Science and Controlling Science

Official experimental science tends by its nature to be interfering, intrusive, actively arranging, even meddling and disrupting. But it is supposed to be cool, neutral, noninterfering,
not changing the nature of what it studies. We know, however,
that this is often not so. For one thing, classical science with
its unconscious bias toward atomism has most often assumed
that it has to dissect in order to know. This is coming to be
less true, but it is still a powerful bias. More subtly, the technique of controlled experimentation is just that—control; that
is to say, it is active manipulating, designing, arranging, and
prearranging.

There is no implication here that this is necessarily bad or
unnecessary. I attempt merely to show that interfering science
is not synonymous with science itself; other strategies are also
possible. The scientist has other methods available to him, and
there are other approaches to knowledge. The one that I want
to describe here is the Taoistic approach to learning about the
nature of things, *not,* I must stress again, as an exclusive
method or as a panacea or as a rival to active science. A good
scientist with two methods available to him, either of which he
can use as he sees fit, is more powerful that a good scientist
with only one method at his disposal.

It may be a little inexact to call Taoistic receptivity a technique, for it consists essentially in being able to keep your hands off and your mouth shut, to be patient, to suspend action and be receptive and passive. It stresses careful observation of a noninterfering sort. It is therefore an attitude to nature rather than a technique in the ordinary sense (42). Perhaps even it should be called an antitechnique. When I have described this attitude to my scientific friends, they have usually sniffed and said, "Oh yes, simple descriptive science." But often I am not at all sure they have got my meaning.

Real receptivity of the Taoistic sort is a difficult achievement. To be able to listen—really, wholly, passively, self-effacingly listen—without presupposing, classifying, improving, controverting, evaluating, approving or disapproving, without dueling with what is being said, without rehearsing the rebuttal in advance, without free-associating to portions of what is being said so that succeeding portions are not heard at all—such listening is rare. Children are abler than their parents to look and to listen in an absorbed and selfless way. Kurt Wolff has called it "surrender" in his articles (82), which are difficult and complex enough to knock out of anyone's head the notion that surrender is easy.

To order a person to be receptive, or Taoistic, or to "surrender," is like telling the tense person that he must relax. He's willing to, but he just doesn't know how. Serenity, composure, calmness, repose, peacefulness, relaxation—perhaps such words as these will better convey my meaning, although they are not quite right either. In any case they do carry the implication that fear, tension, anger, and impatience are the enemies of receptiveness and noninterference, that one must be able to respect what one is examining or learning about. One must be able to let it be itself, to defer to it, even to approve of its being itself, and to feel reward and even joy in watching it be itself, i.e., unfolding its own inner nature, undisturbed and unchanged by the nature of the observer, unintruded upon. Much of the world may be said to be shy in the sense implied here that an animal or a child is shy and in the sense that only the self-effacing observer will be permitted to see the secrets.

Eastern writers have stressed more the concept of the observer's harmony with the nature that he studies. Here the stress is a little different, for it is implied that the observer is himself part of the nature he observes. He fits in, he belongs, he is at home. He is part of the scene rather than a spectator of a diorama. In a sense he studies his mother while he is in his mother's arms. Destroying, changing, manipulating, and controlling are then clearly arrogant and out of place. Mastery of nature is not the only possible relation to it for a scientist.

We in the West often accept a receptive, noninterfering attitude in certain areas of life, so at least we can understand what is meant here, what it feels like simply to observe and to absorb receptively. The examples I first think of are looking at art and listening to music. In these areas we do not intrude or interfere. We simply enjoy by being receptive, by surrendering to and fusing with the music, for example, to which we "give in" and which we let be itself. We are also able to absorb warmth from the sun or in a tub of warm water without doing anything about it. Some of us are good patients and are able to regress nicely with doctors and nurses. Women are supposed to be yielding and surrendering in sex, in childbirth, in mothering, in being led in dancing. Most of us can be happily passive before a good fire or a beautiful river or forest. And obviously a masterful attitude is not the way to endear yourself to a strange society or to a therapeutic patient.

For some reason, however, the receptive strategy of knowing is not much talked about in the textbooks and is not highly esteemed as a scientific technique. This is peculiar because there are many areas of knowledge for which such an attitude is essential. I think particularly of the ethnologist, the clinical psychologist, the ethologist, the ecologist, but the receptive strategy is useful in principle in all areas.

Of course, making the distinction between suchness and abstractness and then integrating them with each other confronts us again with the old problem of the reality of universals and laws. Are they entirely manmade, invented by him for his own convenience? Or are they discovered rather than created? Are they a perception, however dim, of something out there which existed before men did? Without attempting any definitive answer here, it is yet possible to contribute something to the clarification of the question.

First of all, the dichotomous, either-or phrasing of the question should automatically arouse our suspicions. Can this not be a matter of degree? The distinction between suchness and abstraction suggests that it is. It is true that the perception of suchness is far more Taoistic, receptive, and passive than is the achievement of integration and abstractions. But this does not necessarily mean, as many have thought, that the perception of universals is *only* an active task, a creation by fiat. It can also be a receptive openness, a noninterfering willingness for things to be themselves, an ability to wait patiently for the inner structure of percepts to reveal themselves to us, a finding of order rather than an ordering.

The best known operation of this kind is Freud's discovery of (and recommendation of) "free-floating attention." In trying to understand a therapeutic patient—or, for that matter, any person—it turns out to be most efficient in the long run to give up active concentration and striving to understand quickly. The danger here is of a premature explanation or theory, which, furthermore, is likely to be too much one's own construction or creation. Striving, concentration, and focusing of attention are not the best ways to perceive at the preconscious or unconscious level, in terms of primary process. These are secondary processes and may actually conceal or push out primary-process data. The psychoanalyst's injunction is, "Let the unconscious speak to (and listen to) the unconscious."

Something similar is true for the ethnologist trying to understand a culture in all its intricacy. Here, too, the premature theory is dangerous, for it may make it impossible to perceive thereafter anything that contradicts the premature construct. Better to be patient, to be receptive, to "surrender" to the data, to let them fall into place in their own way. So also for ethology, for ecology, and for the field naturalist. So also in principle for anyone dealing with large masses of data of any kind. One learns to be not only active but also passive. One arranges and rearranges and fiddles with data, looking at the tables idly, playfully, in a daydreaming way, unhurriedly, again and again. One "sleeps on it," referring the whole business to the unconscious. And the history of scientific discoveries shows that often enough this works well.

In a word, the construction of theories and laws is often rather like a *discovery* of them. There seems to be an interplay and a joining of activity and receptivity, and it seems best for any knower, lay or professional, to be able to be both active and receptive as the situation demands.

## CONTEMPLATION

In any case, what *can* you do with the "way things are," with the sheer suchness of the world and of the things in it— granting, of course, that you are not frightened by it all (as many people are)? About the only thing you can do when you are passively receptive and accepting is to wonder at it all, contemplate it, savor it, marvel at it, be fascinated with it—hopefully, enjoy it. That is, the thing to do is to do nothing. This is about the way children experience the concrete world, intently, absorbed, spellbound, popeyed, enchanted. In peak experiences and in desolation experiences, too, some version of this gluing to the world can happen. So also as we contemplate death or are reprieved from it, or when love opens us up to the world and it to us, or when the psychedelic drugs have their best effects, or when a poet or a painter can manage to refreshen the world for us—these are all roads to the perception of the suchness and realness of things. And all of them join in teaching us that it need not be only frightening, as so many assume, but also can be profoundly beautiful and lovable.

For the moment, at least, we don't have to *do* anything about multiplicity; we can just experience it receptively, Taoistically, contemplatively. It doesn't at once have to be explained, classified, theorized about, or even understood (except in its own terms).

Some people claim, we should remember, that in such moments we are closest to reality. If we want to witness reality most nakedly, this is the way to do it, they tell us. They warn that as we begin to organize, to classify, to simplify, to abstract, and to conceptualize, so do we begin to move away from reality as it is, perceiving instead our own constructions and inventions, our own preconceptions. These are our own housekeeping arrangements by which we impose order on a chaotic and disorderly world for our own convenience.

Such an attitude is the direct opposite of the customary scientific position in which, for instance, the table that Eddington saw and touched was less real to him than the table that the physicists conceptualized. Most physicists think of themselves as getting closer and closer to reality as they leave the world of sensory qualities further and further behind them.

But there is no question about it: they certainly are involved with a reality different from the one in which their wives and children live. Going simpleward does dissolve *this* reality.

We needn't arbitrate this disagreement, since we have already agreed that science has the two poles of experiencing and comprehending concreteness and also of organizing the welter of concreteness into graspable abstractions. There is however, the fact that the former goal needs stressing today and the latter does not. Scientists usually do not think of themselves as receptive contemplators, but they should, or else they risk losing their footing in the experiential reality with which all knowledge and all science begins.

The word and the concept "contemplation" can, then, be understood as a form of nonactive, noninterfering witnessing and savoring. That is, it can be assimilated to Taoistic, nonintruding, receptivity to the experience. In such a moment the experience happens instead of being made to happen. Since this permits it to be itself, minimally distorted by the observer, it is in certain instances a path to more reliable and more veridical cognition.

# 11

## Interpersonal (I-Thou) Knowledge as a Paradigm for Science

Historically science first concerned itself with physical impersonal, inanimate things—planets, falling objects—and with equally impersonal mathematics. It went on to study living things in the same spirit, and finally about a century ago it deliberately brought the human being into the laboratory to study him in the same ways that had already proved so successful. He was to be studied as an object dispassionately, neutrally, quantitatively, in controlled experimental situations. The choice of "problem" tended to be whatever was susceptible to handling in this way. (Of course, at the same time an entirely different kind of psychology was evolving among psychiatrists in the clinic, out of an entirely different tradition and with different laws, rules, and methods.)

The "scientific" study of the human being was simply a more difficult, more exasperating application of the methodology of physics, astronomy, biology, etc., to an irritatingly unsuitable object. He was a special case, so to speak, a peripheral example on the edge of impersonal scientific method. I propose that instead of this impersonal centering point we take the human person as the starting or centering point. Let us try to take knowledge of the person as the model case from which to create paradigms or models of methodology, conceptualization, and *Weltanschauung,* of philosophy and epistemology.

What are the consequences (for the moment) of taking as the ultimate bit of knowledge that which occurs in the I-Thou, interpersonal, Agapean-love relationships between two people. Let us think of this knowledge as "normal," "basic," routine, as our basic measuring stick to judge how "knowledgy" any bit of knowledge is. Examples, not always reciprocal, are a friend knowing a friend, two persons loving each other, a parent knowing a child, or a child knowing a parent, a brother knowing a brother, a therapist knowing a patient, etc. In such relationships it is characteristic that the knower is involved with what he knows. He is not distant; he is close. He is not cool about it; he is warm. He is not unemotional; he is emotional. He has empathy, intuition for the object of knowledge, i.e., he feels identified with it, the same as it, to some degree and in some manner identical with it. He cares.

The good mother can often communicate better with her child than pediatricians or psychologists can. If these doctors have any sense, they use her as an interpreter or translator, and often enough they ask, "What is he trying to say?" Long time friends, especially married ones, understand each other, predict and communicate with each other in ways totally mysterious to spectators.

The ultimate limit, the completion toward which this kind of interpersonal knowledge moves, is through intimacy to the mystical fusion in which the two people become one in a phenomenological way that has been best described by mystics, Zen Buddhists, peak experiencers, lovers, estheticians, etc. In this experience of fusion a knowing of the other comes about through *becoming* the other, i.e., it becomes experiential knowledge from within. I know it because I know myself, and it has now become part of myself. Fusion with the object of knowledge permits experiential knowledge. And since experiential knowledge is the best kind of knowledge for many human purposes, a good mode of cognizing an object is to move toward fusion with it. And certainly since a good move toward fusion with anyone is to care for him and even to love him, we wind up with a "law" of learning and cognizing: Do you want to know? Then care!

Less extreme than mystical fusion is the therapeutic growth relationship. I confine myself here to all the insight-uncovering, Taoistic, nondirective therapies, e.g., Freud, Rogers, existential therapy. Much has been written about transference, encounter, unconditional positive regard, and the like, but all have in common the explicit awareness of the necessity of a particular kind of relationship that dispels fear, that permits the one receiving therapy to see himself more truly and thus gives him control over self-approved and self-disapproved aspects of himself.

Let us now consider this therapeutic and growth relationship primarily as a method for acquiring knowledge. And then let us contrast this cognitive tool with a microscope or a telescope:

| THE MICROSCOPE OR TELESCOPE (SPECTATOR-KNOWLEDGE) | THE THERAPEUTIC RELATIONSHIP (INTERPERSONAL-RELATIONSHIP-KNOWLEDGE) |
|---|---|
| Involves a split between subject and object, the so-called "Cartesian split." This split and "distancing" are considered good, useful, necessary for the purpose. | Moves toward lessening this split and this "distancing" on the part of both therapist and patient, each in a different way but toward the same purpose of better understanding of the patient rather than the therapist. |

The ideal is perfect detachment of the spectator sort, perfect "othering" of each other. Not identified, disengaging, disentangling.

The ideal is fusion, melting, merging.

The observer is a stranger, an alien, a nonparticipant.

The observer is a participant-observer.

Less reafference and commerce-with. My view of a table, or of a sculpture. More alienation and less identification-with.

More reafference and commerce-with. A carpenter's view of the table that he has made. A sculptor's view of a sculpture. Less alienation and more identification-with.

Trying to be unrelated and to avoid the relationship (in order to be able to be a neutral judge).

Trying to be related and more intimate.

Unawareness of and no use of split between experiencing ego and self-observing ego. No use of self-knowledge in the cognitive process.

Specific enhancement of the interplay between experiencing ego and self-observing ego and of their fruitful dependence and independence. Self-knowledge is an essential part of this cognitive process.

The nature and uniqueness of the observer is not a great problem. Any competent observer is as good as any other and will see the same truths.

The nature of the knower is a *sine qua non* of the nature of the known. Knowers are not easily interchangeable.

The observer is not seen as creating the truths in any important way. He discovers, witnesses, or perceives them.

The observer in part creates the truth by being what he is and who he is and by doing what he is doing.

Laissez-faire (uncaring) cognition.

Ultimately (Taoistic) non-interfering cognition that emerges from caring.

I-It (Buber).

I-Thou (Buber).

More mental activity, theorizing, hypothesizing, guessing, classifying.

More receptivity, more willingness to experience purely before permitting secondary processes to take over.

Active attention, willed concentration. Purposefulness.

Free-floating attention, patience, waiting. Primary process, preconscious, unconscious.

Entirely conscious, rational, verbal.

Primary process, preconscious, unconscious, preverbal.

Spectator detachment, neutrality, and objectivity of noninvolvement, noncaring of *laissez faire*. It doesn't make any difference what the intrinsic nature of the percept may be.

Detachment and objectivity of noninterference, of caring, enjoying, willingness to let the person be himself. Cognition of the being of the other (B-Cognition). No illusions about the person, realistic perceiving, nondenying, no need to improve the percept, no a priori demands upon it. Accepting its suchness. Keeping hands off because one loves the way it is, wants it to be itself, and doesn't want it to be other than it is.

The percept is perceived. The histological slide, the microscope, and the biologist all go their own way. They are divorced. Neither the micro-

The perceived responds back. It is grateful for being understood. It demands to be properly perceived. It projects fantasies and hopes upon the

scope nor the slide falls in love with the biologist.

perceiver. It gives a halo to the perceiver. The perceived loves the perceiver and may cling to him. Or the perceived may hate or be ambivalent about the perceiver. The person has something to say about the "cognitive tool." This in him can change the "cognizer" (counter-transference, etc.).

Knowing persons is complicated by the fact that so much of their motivational lives are interpersonal. The basic needs are satisfied or frustrated generally by other people. If you are trying to understand another person, it is better if he feels unthreatened with you, if he feels you accept, understand, and like him, perhaps even love him, if he feels that you respect him, and if he feels that you do not threaten his freedom to be himself. If on the other hand you dislike him or disrespect him, if you feel contempt or disapproval, if you look down on him, or if you "rubricize" him, i.e., if you refuse to see him as an individual (*43*, ch. 9), then the person will close off much of himself and refuse to let himself be seen. (This is on about the same principle that makes me show you the pictures of my children if you love children. It you do not like children, I will not want to show them to you.) He may even with secret malice deliberately give you wrong information. This happens often enough to ethnologists, psychotherapists, sociologists, public opinion pollers, child psychologists, and many others.

There is a large research literature to support such conclusions, e.g., on interviewing, on the techniques of psychotherapy, on ethnological practice, on public-opinion polling, on being understood, on interperson perception, on interrelations between the strong and the weak, etc. But offhand I don't remember that these research findings have been applied to the epistemological problem of "acquiring" reliable and veridical knowledge. I suspect that few people in these areas of research are aware of this particular application of their findings, or perhaps they *are* aware but are overawed by the implications. This is understandable. We have been taught and re-taught that *the* path to reliable knowledge is always the same whether you wish to study molecules or men. And now we are being told that maybe there are different paths for these two kinds of study. Occasionally there is even an implication that maybe the technique for studying humans may be generalized one day so as to *include* the study of molecules, so that we may even wind up again with a monistic epistemology but with a different centering point!

Something of this sort, this acquiring of knowledge through an interpersonal relationship of intimacy between knower and known, also happens, perhaps in lesser degree, in other areas of science. Ethology comes to mind at once. But all forms of knowledge derived "clinically" by physicians share some of these characteristics also. So does social anthropology. So do many branches of sociology, political science, economics, history, and possibly all the social sciences. Perhaps also we could add all or many of the linguistic sciences.

But I wish to make a more important point. It is not necessary to "choose up sides" or to vote a straight party ticket. It is true that we could make a hierarchy of sciences or of all areas of knowledge, ranging from greatest to least involvement in a relationship. But I wish to raise the more radical question: can *all* the sciences, *all* knowledge be conceptualized as a resultant of a loving or caring interrelationship between knower and known? What would be the advantages to us of setting this epistemology alongside the one that now reigns in "objective science"? Can we simultaneously use both?

My own feeling is that we can and should use both epistemologies as the situation demands. I do not see them as contradictory but as enriching each other. There is no reason not to include both weapons in the armory of any knower who wants to know *anything*. We must entertain the possibility that even the astronomer or geologist or chemist might be able to perceive more wholly even that which is least personal. I mean the conscious, verbalized, formulated possibility, because I am already convinced that some astronomers and some chemists, etc. secretly relate to their "problems" in ways analogous to those of lovers to their loved ones.

### "LOVE FOR" THE OBJECT OF STUDY

The meaning of "love for" the object to be known, understood, and appreciated has to be seen more clearly in its complexities. At the least it must mean "interest in" the object of study. It is difficult to see or hear that which is totally uninteresting or boring. It is also difficult to think about it, to remember it, to keep oneself at the job, to stick to it. All the defensive and resistive powers of the person can be mobilized into action when one is forced by some external pressure to study something totally uninteresting. One forgets, one thinks of other things, the mind wanders, fatigue sets in, intelligence seems to diminish. In a word, one is likely to do a poor job unless one is minimally interested in the task and drawn to it. At least a little passion (or libidinizing) seems to be needed.

True, it is possible to be dutiful, and even a child will do many jobs in school without interest or with only external interest in order to please the teacher. But such children bring up other problems, too profound to go into here, of training of the character, of the enriching of autonomy, of the dangers of mere docility. I mention them because I do not wish to fall into the black-white dichotomy that is so easy here. In any case there is little question about the simple statement that for the best learning, perceiving, understanding, and remembering of a person, it is desirable to be interested, involved, to have "a little bit of love," to be at least a little fascinated and drawn.

So far as the scientist is concerned, he knows that this is true for him if only because scientific study especially needs patience, stubbornness, stick-to-it-iveness, unswerving concentration on the task, the fortitude to overcome inevitable disappointments, etc. This is a minimal statement. What is really needed for long-time scientific success is passion, fascination, obsession. The fruitful scientist is the one who talks about his "problem" in about the same spirit as he does about the woman he loves, as an end rather than as a means to other ends. Rising above all distractions and becoming lost in his work means that he is not divided. All his intelligence is available for the one purpose that he is entirely given to. He gives it everything he's got.[1]

This can be meaningfully called an act of love, and there are certain definite advantages in such a phrasing. Similarly it is meaningful to expect better work from the one who loves his work and his problem. This is why I think it will help us, even as scientists in the strictest sense, to study carefully the paradigm of "knowledge through love" that we can see most purely in lovers or in the parent-child relationship or, suitably translated into naturalistic terms, in theological and mystical literature.

### THE MAKING OF TRUTH IN THE INTERPERSONAL RELATION

The picture of truth and of reality that we have inherited from the classical science of the impersonal is that it is "out

---

[1] "If you want an absolute duffer in an investigation, you must, after all, take the man who has no interest whatever in its results; he is the warranted incapable, the positive fool." (William James)

there," perfect, complete, hidden but uncoverable. In the earlier versions the observer simply observed. In later versions it was understood that the observer had spectacles that distorted but which could never be removed. Most recently physicists and psychologists have learned that the act of observation is itself a shaper, a changer, an intruder into the phenomenon being observed. In a word, the observer partly creates the reality, i.e., the truth. Reality seems to be a kind of alloy of the perceiver and the perceived, a sort of mutual product, a transaction. For instance, see the many researches with reafference and with the effects of observer-expectation, to mention only two well-known lines of experimentation.

I mean here more than the "personal equation" of the astronomer or even Heisenberg's principle of indeterminacy. I refer rather to the impossibility of finding out what, for example, a preliterate culture would "really" be like, undistorted by the observing ethnologist. Or to take an example I was recently involved in, how can you subtract the admittedly dampening effect of an outside observer from the "true" behavior of a store-front religious group? There was a story, probably apocryphal, that I heard during my college days, of a group of fraternity boys who agreed, for fun, to rush a homely, awkward wallflower of a girl. The story was that the rushing changed her into a confidently feminine and lovely girl, so that the boys fell in love with their own creation.

## EMOTION AND TRUTH

I quote from David L. Watson's *The Study of Human Nature:* "When two men are arguing, I do not find that the truth of the matter always rests with the more dispassionate participant. Passion may enhance the disputants' powers of expression and thus lead, in the long run, to deeper regions of truth" (p. 187–188). "It is beyond question that *certain kinds* of emotion entirely distort our judgment. But I would ask the rationalist extremists: would we *have* any science, if truth did not inspire passionate devotion in the searcher?" (p. 188).

This is a characteristic expression of the rising discontent among psychologists with the old and widely held notion that emotions are *only* disrupting, that they are the enemy of true perception and good judgment, that they are the opposite of sagacity and are and must be mutually excluding of truth. A humanistic approach to science generates a different attitude, i.e., that emotion can be synergic with cognition, and a help in truth-finding.

### FUSION-KNOWLEDGE

These love relationships that can go over into the mystic experience of fusion with the world give us our end point (*beyond* knowledge through love for the object) of knowledge by fusion with the object, by becoming one with it. This can then be considered for theoretical purposes to become experiential knowledge, knowledge from within, by *being* what we are knowing. At least this is the ideal limit to which such knowledge approaches or tries to approach.

This is not so far-out as it may sound. A respectable way of studying schizophrenia is to try to *be* schizophrenic temporarily by the use of appropriate chemicals, or to have been schizophrenic and recovered. One can then more easily identify with the schizophrenic. One of the most loved and respected of the neobehavioristic rat psychologists, Edward Tolman, admitted once in defiance of his own official theorizing that when he wanted to predict what a rat would do, he tried to identify with the rat, to feel like one, and then to ask himself, "Now what would I do?" Much of what we know about Communists has been taught us by reformed Communists, who can remember how it felt to be one. The same would be true for John Birchers, and I await eagerly such a retrospective account of how it felt to be a John Bircher.

Another kind of example, following the same paradigm in a different field, is that of the ethnologist. You can learn many facts about a tribe that you dislike or by whom you are disliked, but there are definite limits to what you can then get to know. In order to know your Indians rather than merely to know about them, you have to melt into the culture to some extent. If you "become" a Blackfoot Indian, then you can answer many questions simply by introspection.

Even at the impersonal extreme it is possible to differentiate the two feels of looking through a telescope. One can peep through the telescope at the moon, like a peeping Tom (spectator, outsider) peeping through a keyhole at the alien, the distant, the other, the far away (which we are not and never can be). Or you can sometimes forget yourself, get absorbed, fascinated, and be out there in the middle of what you are looking at, *in* that world rather than outside it peering in. This can be likened to the difference between being a member of a family and being an orphan out in the dark cold street, wistfully looking in through the window at the warm family inside. Colin Wilson's books are full of examples of outsiders and wistful peepers (*80*).

Similarly one can be within the microscopic world, or one can be outside it, looking with your eye through the microscope at the slide that is an object out there. You can listen to organ music judiciously, calmly examining it to hear how good it is and whether it is worth the money you paid for the ticket. Or you can suddenly get caught up by it and become the music and feel it pulse through your insides, so that you are not in some other place. If you are dancing and the rhythm "gets you," you can slip over to being inside the rhythm. You can identify with the rhythm. You can become its willing instrument.

## TWO KINDS OF OBJECTIVITY

The term "scientific objectivity" has, in effect, been pre-empted by the physics-centered theorists of science and bent to the use of their mechanomorphic *Weltanschauung*. It was certainly necessary for astronomers and physicists to assert their freedom to see what was before their eyes rather than having truth determined a priori by the church or the state. This is the kernel of sense in the concept of "value-free science." But it is this generalization, uncritically accepted today by many, that has crippled so many human and social scientists.

Of course, these students are now willing to study other people's values, from which the investigator can presumably detach himself and which can be studied as unemotionally as the "values" of ants or trees. That is, they can be treated as "facts," and thus they can become amenable at once to "normal" treatment by all the methods and concepts of classical, impersonal science. But this is not the real issue.

The point of this kind of "scientific objectivity" is clear; it is to guard against the projection into the perceived of human or supernatural motives or emotions or preconceptions which are not "there" in fact and therefore should not be seen as being there. Observe that this necessary rule of science to "see only what is actually there" (which began as *not* seeing "God's design" or Aristotle's dicta or human purposes in inanimate objects or in animals) is today primarily an effort to guard against the projection of the scientists' *own* values or hopes or wishes.

Though this can never be done perfectly, it can yet be approached in degree. Normal scientific training and normal scientific methods are efforts to get closer and closer to this impossible terminus. There is no doubt that this effort does in fact succeed to an extent. The person we call a good scientist is marked by his greater ability to perceive that which he dislikes and by his great skepticism when he perceives something that he approves of.

The question is: how possible is this goal? What is the best way of perceiving something as it is, least contaminated by our own hopes, fears, wishes, goals? And most important: is there only one path to this goal? Is there another path to "objectivity," that is, to seeing things as they really are?

Classically, "scientific objectivity" has been most successfully achieved when its objects were most distant from human aspirations, hopes, and wishes. It is easy to feel uninvolved, detached, clear-eyed, and neutral if one is studying the nature of rocks or heat or electrical currents. One doesn't identify with a moon. One doesn't "care" about it as one does about one's child. It is easy to take the laissez-faire attitude with oxygen or hydrogen and to have noninterfering curiosity, to be Taoistically receptive, to let things be themselves. To be blunt about it, it is easy to be neutrally objective, fair, and just when you don't care about the outcome, when you can't identify or sympathize, when you neither love or hate.

But what happens with this framework of ideas and attitudes when we move over into the human and social realm, when we try to be objective about people we love or hate, about our loyalties or values, about our very selves? We are then no longer laissez-faire, impersonal, uninvolved, unidentified, without stakes. Accordingly it becomes far more difficult to be "laissez-faire objective" or "not-caring objective." Now there are new hazards.

In the effort to achieve "scientific," i.e., uninvolved, laissez-faire, don't-care objectivity, the anthropologist, for instance, may buy the whole package that he mistakenly ties to this kind of objectivity. He may become scientistic rather than scientific, may feel it necessary to drown his human feelings for the people he studies, may quantify whether necessary or not, and may wind up with accurate details and a false whole. (The best approach to reading in ethnology is still a discreet mix of technical monographs, the better travel reports, and the impressionistic writings of the more poetic and humanistic anthropologists.)

Granted that not-caring objectivity can be enhanced to some extent by improved training; more important by far is the possibility of another kind of objectivity that comes from caring rather than from not caring. This is the kind which I have already described in various publications as a consequence of Being-Love, of peak experiences, of unitive perception, of self-actualization, of synergy, of Taoistic receptivity, of the "creative attitude," of Being-Cognition, and as one general aspect of a psychology of being, and that Nameche (56) has also analyzed fruitfully.

Briefly stated, my thesis is: if you love something or someone enough at the level of Being, then you can enjoy its actualization of itself, which means that you will not want to interfere with it, since you love it as it is in itself. You will then be able to perceive it in a noninterfering way, which means leaving it alone. This in turn means that you will be able to see it as is, uncontaminated by your selfish wishes, hopes, demands, anxieties, or preconceptions. Since you love it as it is in itself, neither will you be prone to judge it, use it, improve it, or in any other way to project your own values into it. This also tends to mean more concrete experiencing and witnessing; less abstracting, simplifying, organizing, or intellectual manipulation. Leaving it alone to be itself also implies a more holistic, global attitude and less active dissecting. It adds up to this: you may be fond enough of someone to dare to see him just as he is; if you love something the way it is, you won't change it. Therefore you may then see it (or him) as it is in its own nature, untouched, unspoiled, i.e., objectively. The greater your Being-Love of the person, the less your need to be blind.

Another aspect of this "caring objectivity" can be phrased in terms of transcendence. If objectivity includes among its meanings being able to see things as they are whether we like them or not, whether we approve of them or not, whether they are good or bad, then one becomes abler to achieve this standpoint the more one is able to transcend these distinctions. This is difficult to do, but it is more or less possible in Being-Cognition, for instance, and in Being-Love, etc. It is also difficult to communicate, but since I have tried in other writings, I won't pursue it further here (see also 56).

To take only a single illustration, these two kinds of objectivity and their complementary quality are well exemplified in the undoubted advantages and the equally undoubted disadvantages of being an outsider. The Jew or the Negro has far more spectator objectivity about our society than has the insider. If you belong to the country club or the establishment, you are likely to take all its values for granted and not even notice them. This includes all the rationalizations, the denials, the official hypocrisies, etc. Just these the outsider (80) can see clearly and easily. There are therefore some truths that the spectator can see more easily than the experiencer, who is part of the reality to be cognized.

On the other hand, there is much evidence which I have already mentioned that in certain respects Negroes are better knowers of Negroes than whites are, etc. There is by now no need to repeat this.

Another fascinating set of research questions and hypotheses is generated also by the concept of "knowledge through Being-love." The ability to B-love is characteristic of a higher level of personal maturity. Therefore personal maturity is a precondition for this kind of perspicuity, and one way to improve this kind of knowing would be to improve the maturity of the knower. What could this imply for the education of scientists?

# 12

## Value-Free Science?

In my *Religions, Values and Peak-Experiences* I pointed out that both orthodox science and orthodox religion have been institutionalized and frozen into a mutually excluding dichotomy. This separation into Aristotelian *a* and *not-a* has been almost perfect, as if a line had been drawn between them in the way that Spain and Portugal once divided the new world between themselves by drawing a geographical line. Every question, every answer, every method, every jurisdiction, every task has been assigned to either one or the other, with practically no overlaps.

One consequence is that they are both pathologized, split into sickness, ripped apart into a crippled half-science and a crippled half-religion. This either-or split forces a kind of either-or choice between them, as if one were confronted with a two-party system in which there is no alternative to voting a straight ticket and choosing one means giving up the other altogether.

As a result of this forced either-or choice, the student who becomes a scientist automatically gives up a great deal of life, especially its richest portions. He is like a monk who is asked to enter a monastery and to make vows of renunciation (because orthodox science has defined out of its jurisdiction so many portions of the real human world).

The most important parceling out of jurisdictions is that science has nothing to do with values. Orthodox science has been defined as value-free, as having nothing to say about the ends, the goals, the purposes, the rewards, or the justifications of life. A common phrasing is "science can tell us nothing about why, only about how." Another is "science is not an ideology or an ethic or a value system; it cannot help us to choose between good and evil." The unavoidable implication is, then, that science is only an instrument, only a technology, to be used equally by either good men or by villains. The Nazi concentration camps are an instance. Another implication is that being a good scientist is compatible with being a good Nazi; one role exerts no intrinsic strain on the other. When the existentialists ask why we should not commit suicide, the orthodox scientist can only shrug his shoulders and say, "Why not?" (Just so we don't get confused here, notice that I am not talking about a priori "should" or "ought": organisms make a choice between life or death; they prefer life and hang on to it; but it cannot be said of oxygen or electromagnetic waves or gravitation that they have preferences in this same sense).

This situation is now even worse than it was during the Renaissance, because more recently all the value fields, all the humanities and all the arts, have been included in this world of nonscience, that is, of the unscientific. Science began originally as a determination to rely on one's own eyes instead of on the ancients or upon ecclesiastical authority or pure logic. That is, it was originally just a kind of looking for oneself rather than trusting anyone else's preconceived ideas. Nobody then said anything about science being value-free. This was a later accretion.

Orthodox science today attempts to be free not only of values but also of emotions. As youngsters would say, it tries to be "cool." The basic notions of detachment and objectivity, of precision, rigor, and quantification, of parsimony, and of lawfulness, all imply that emotion and emotional intensity are contaminants of cognition. The unquestioned assumption is that "cool" perceiving and neutral thinking are best for discovering any kind of scientific truth. As a matter of fact, many scientists are not even aware that there are other modes of cognition. An important by-product of this dichotomizing is the desacralizing of science, the banishment of all the experiences of transcendence from the realm of the respectably known and the respectably knowable, and the denial of a systematic place in science for awe, wonder, mystery, ecstasy, beauty, and peak experiences.

## VALUES IN SCIENCE

"For example a psychologist may describe a subject's thinking as paranoid but nevertheless . . . refrains from expressing judgments of value regarding such behavior. On the other hand, the philosopher, whose task it is to express value judgments, states whether or not paranoid thinking is good or bad, true or false, desirable or undesirable, etc. . . . This distinction delineates philosophy from all other sciences. Philosophers evaluate; they state whether a person, his behavior or character, is good or bad, right or wrong, beautiful or ugly; in fact, this is precisely the way Plato defined philosophy, namely, the study of the true, the good, the beautiful. Scientists refrain from evaluations since they consider the practice unscientific, and rightly so. . . . Only philosophers evaluate, while scientists describe facts as accurately as they possibly can."[1]

Obviously this statement needs many qualifications. The distinction is too simple. Far more subtle differentiations are necessary, even though we may accept the general tenor of the

[1] Sahakian, W., and M. Sahakian, *Realms of Philosophy* (Schenkman Publishing Co., 1965), pp. 3, 4.

statement, i.e., that in general scientists do less evaluating than nonscientists and are perhaps also more concerned with description than nonscientists—although I doubt that you could convince an artist of this.

For one thing the whole scientific process is itself shot through with selectiveness, choice, and preference. We could even call it gambling if we wanted to, as well as good taste, judgment, and connoisseurship. No scientist is a mere camera eye or tape recorder. He is not indiscriminate in his activities. He doesn't do just anything. He works at problems that he characterizes as "important" or as "interesting," and he comes up with "elegant" or "beautiful" solutions. He does "pretty" experiments, and prefers "simpler" and "cleaner" results to confused or sloppy ones.

All these are value words, evaluating, selecting, preferring, implying a more desirable and a less desirable, not only in the strategy and tactics of the scientist but also in his motivations and goals. Polanyi (60) has set forth most convincingly the thesis that a scientist is at all times a gambler, a connoisseur, a man of good taste or bad taste, a man who makes acts of faith and leaps of commitment, a man of will, a responsible person, an active agent, a chooser and therefore a rejector.

All of these statements go double for the "good" scientist (as compared with the run-of-the-mill, average-to-poor scientist). That is, intelligence being held equal, the scientist we admire and value more highly and the one who is honored by his fellows and by the historians is even more characterizable as a man with good taste and good judgment, a man who has correct hunches, who trusts them and who can act courageously on them, a man who somehow can smell out the good problems, devise beautiful ways of putting them to the test, and can somehow come up with elegantly simple, true, and conclusive answers. The poor scientist doesn't know the difference between an important problem and an unimportant one, a good technique and a poor one, an elegant demonstration and a crude one. In a word, he doesn't know how to evaluate. He lacks good taste. And he does not have hunches that turn out to be correct. Or if he has them, they frighten him, and he turns away from them.

But beyond this insistence that choosing necessarily implies principles of choice, i.e., values, there is the even more obvious point that the whole enterprise of science is concerned with "Truth." That's what science is all about. Truth is considered intrinsically desirable, valuable, beautiful. And of course truth has always been counted among the ultimate values. That is to say, science is in the service of a value, and so are all scientists (9,10,11).

And if I wished I could involve other values in this discussion since it looks probable that the full, ultimate "Truth" is finally definable, only and altogether, by all the other ultimate values. That is, truth is ultimately beautiful, good, simple, comprehensive, perfect, unifying, alive, unique, necessary, final, just, orderly, effortless, self-sufficient, and amusing (44). If it is less than these, it is not yet the fullest degree and quality of truth.

But there are still other meanings for the statements about science being value-free or not value-free. For the psychologists one such issue is no longer in question. It is possible to study in fruitful ways the values of human beings. This is true in the most obvious way: e.g., we have the Allport-Vernon-Lindzey test for values which enables us to say crudely that a person prefers religious values, for instance, to political or esthetic ones. It is equally true, though less obvious, that the many studies of the food preferences of monkeys, for example, can be considered to be descriptions of what is valuable to the animal. So also for the free-choice and self-choice experiments that have been done in many areas. Any studies of choice or preference or selection may be considered to be, in a particular and useful sense, the study of values, either instrumental or final.

The crucial question to be asked is: can science discover the values by which men should live? I think it can, and I have advanced this thesis in various places, supporting it with whatever data I could muster (*40, 43, 44, 46, 48, 50, 51*). This support has been sufficient to convince me, but not yet more skeptical people. It had best be presented as a thesis, programmatic in nature, plausible enough to warrant attention but not solidly enough supported to be accepted as fact.

The data I turn to first are the accumulated experiences of dynamic psychotherapy, starting with Freud and continuing up to the present day in most therapies that have to do with discovering the identity, or the Real Self. I would prefer to call them all the "uncovering therapies" or Taoistic therapies in order to stress that they purport to uncover (more than to construct) the deepest self which has been covered over by bad habits, misconceptions, neuroticizing, etc. All these therapies agree in finding that this most real self partly consists of needs, wishes, impulses, and instinctlike desires. These may be called needs because they must be fulfilled or psychopathology results. As a matter of fact, the historical order of discovery was the other way about. Freud, Adler, Jung, and the rest agreed in this, that in their efforts to understand the origins of adult neurosis, they all wound up with biologically demanding needs violated or neglected early in life. Neurosis seemed to be in its essence a deficiency disease of the same sort that the nutritionists were discovering. And just as the latter, in a kind of reconstructive biology, could finally say, "We have a need for vitamin $B^{12}$," so also can psychotherapists say on the basis of the same kind of data that we have a need to be loved or a need for safety (*50*).

It is these needs, "instinctoid" in nature, that we can also think of as built-in values—values not only in the sense that the organism wants and seeks them but also in the sense that they are both good and necessary for the organism. And it is these values that are found, uncovered—*re*covered, perhaps we should say—in the course of psychotherapy or self-discovery. We may then regard these techniques of therapy and self-discovery as being also cognitive tools or scientific methods (in the sense that they are the best methods we have available today to uncover these particular kinds of data).

It is in this sense at least that I would maintain that science in the broadest sense can and does discover what human values are, what the human being needs in order to live a good and a happy life, what he needs in order to avoid illness, what is good for him and what is bad for him. Apparent discoveries of this sort seem already to exist in great number in all the medical and biological sciences, for instance. But here we have to be careful to distinguish. On the one hand, what the healthy human being chooses, prefers, and values out of his own deepest inner nature, is also most often good for him. On the other hand, physicians may have learned that aspirin is good for headaches, but we have no inborn yearning for aspirin, as we do have for love or for respect.

### SCIENCE AS A SYSTEM OF VALUES

In an interview Ralph Ellison said of his work: "I feel that with my decision to devote myself to the novel I took on one of the responsibilities inherited by those who practice the craft in the U. S.: that of describing for all, that fragment of the huge diverse American experience which I know best, and which offers me the possibility of contributing not only to the growth of the literature but to the shaping of the culture as I should like it to be. The American novel is in this sense a conquest of the frontier; as it describes our experience, it creates it."[2]

This passage well expresses the motivational situation confronting thoughtful scientists as well as novelists. Certainly a main task, even a *sine qua non* for the scientist, is describing a portion of the world for all and contributing to the growth of the scientific literature. Up to this point one just does not ask "why." The scientist does it because he likes doing it, because it is "interesting," because it is fun or exciting, or because he can make an easier and more pleasant living this way than by driving a truck. So far, in effect, he is enjoying himself because he is enjoying himself, and since he supports himself and his family, people raise no objection even if they do not understand what he is doing or why he is doing it.

But observe that if we stop at this point, we cannot yet differentiate him from any other kind of worker who likes doing what he is doing because he likes doing it. For instance, a professional bridge player or a stamp collector or a television announcer or a model also may be doing what he wants to do and is earning a living.

The scientist normally tries to justify his calling not only to the society that supports and protects him but to himself as well, to his friends, to his family. He himself is ordinarily not satisfied with an explanation simply in terms of self-indulgence. He feels and he tries to show, however inarticulately, that his work is valuable beyond his personal pleasures. It has value in itself, for others, for the society, for mankind. And a fair proportion of scientists will tell you that they, too, are "shaping the culture as they would like it to be," i.e., they are Utopians. They have goals in mind that they consider intrinsically good, toward which their work moves. (Of course, this is true for some but not for all.) That is, they are enlisted in the service of a cause. They are not merely selfish.

[2] *Writers At Work: Second Series* (Viking, 1963), p. 344.

There is another sense in which science and scientists are not value-free. They do see a difference between being a scientist and doing television commercials. They do feel virtuous, valuable, and superior. They do regard themselves as living a better life than, let us say, models. Science is good *for* something, and also it is valuable in itself. It is good in itself because it creates more truth, beauty, order, lawfulness, goodness, perfection, unity, etc., and it is certainly an honor to help build so awe-inspiring a structure. It is (or can be) good *for* something because it lengthens life and reduces disease and pain, makes life richer and fuller, reduces back-breaking labor, and could (in principle) make better human beings.

The justification that is used depends on the particular audience that is being persuaded, and the "level" of the justification certainly must be equivalent to the height of development to which the listener has attained. But some justification there usually is and has to be. Science as a human enterprise and as a social institution has goals, ends, ethics, morals, purposes—in a word, values—as Bronowski (*9, 10, 11*) has so conclusively and brilliantly demonstrated.

# 13

## Stages, Levels, and Degrees of Knowledge[1]

In Chapter 8 I talked about improved self-knowledge making better knowers. This has never been "proved" in the ordinary sense. How, then, dare I make such a statement?

I base this statement—for instance—upon thousands of clinical experiences, single individual patients with single therapists as well as the personal reports of the therapists themselves. For most common-sense people this experience is a form of knowledge, even though it has relatively low reliability. There is no question at all that our confidence in this "truth" would be far greater if a carefully planned and designed experiment would report statistically significant superiority of scientists who were more healthy over those who were less healthy, or of scientists who had gone through psychoanalysis, etc. Such data are far more reliable than "clinical experience." But in the absence of such experiments, are we not being realistic and "scientific" if we are quite aware of the degree of confidence that the data warrant, and if we specify this clearly to each other?

Knowledge is a matter of degree. Any increment of knowledge or of reliability is better than nothing. One case is better than none, and two are better than one. Neither knowledge

[1] See esp. Northrop (*59*), Watson (*75, 76*), and Kuhn (*30*).

in general nor reliability in particular is an all-or-none matter. There is no sharp shoreline which marks off the land of knowledge from the ocean of not-knowledge.

There are some who will insist that "scientific" knowledge is and must be clear, lucid, unequivocally defined, unmistakable, demonstrable, repeatable, communicable, logical, rational, verbalizable, conscious. If it is not these, then it is not "scientific"; it is something else. But what shall we say, then, about the first stages of knowledge, the precursors of these final forms, the beginnings that each of us can easily enough experience in himself.

First comes the uneasiness, the restlessness, the unhappiness, the feeling that something is not quite right. This uneasiness can come before it finds its explanation. That is, we can feel something that, if put into words, would run, "I feel uneasy, but I don't know why. There's something not quite right here, but I don't know what it is." To make it even more confusing, this feeling can be totally unconscious or only half conscious, and it may be recognized only sometime later, retrospectively.

At this point all that we have to deal with are hunches, guesses, intuitions, dreams, fantasies, vague "prethoughts" not yet verbalized. Fortuitous associations can send us off in one direction or another. We may suddenly wake out of sleep with an answer that may then be put to the test and may turn out to be either right or wrong. Communication within ourselves or with others is often vague, inconsistent, self-contradictory, illogical, even irrational. It may be couched in figures of speech, metaphors, similes, etc. We may begin researching by sensing a gap and talking about it as a poet talks rather than as a scientist is supposed to talk. And we may then behave more like a physician or a gambler or a teacher than like the traditional scientist.

Think, for instance, of the language of psychoanalysis, with its physical analogies and parallels, reifications, personifications, and half-mythological entities. It is easy to criticize all this from the point of view of finished and elegant science. But—and this is my main point here—these words are the fumbling efforts to communicate intuitive, clinical feelings that cannot yet be expressed in any other way. They are the best that can be done at the present stage of development of knowledge. The best logicians, mathematicians, physicists, chemists, and biologists in the world could do no better if faced with the task of describing, for instance, the phenomena of transference or repression or anxiety. These phenomena exist and have been experienced and reported by thousands of patients in one form or another, and they have been witnessed by thousands of psychotherapists in one version or another. And yet it is impossible to describe them well or even to get agreement on which words to use in descriptions.

It is easy for the laboratory scientist to criticize all this. But in the end these criticisms come down to an accusation that a final state of knowledge has not yet been achieved. This is why inchoate knowledge is apt to be sloppy and ambiguous. *This is a stage through which knowledge must pass!* There is no known alternative. There is no other way to do things.[2]

[2] ". . . Biology will run dry unless it becomes more receptive than it is presently to unsuspected phenomena, unpredictable on the basis of what is already known. Science does not progress only by inductive, analytical knowledge. The imaginative speculations of the mind come first, the verification and the analytical breakdown come only later. And imagination depends upon a state of emotional and intellectual freedom which makes the mind receptive to the impressions that it receives from the world in its confusing, overpowering, but enriching totality. We must try to experience again the receptivity of the young ages of science when it was socially acceptable to marvel. What Baudelaire said of art applies equally well to science: 'Genius is youth recaptured.' More prosaically, I believe that in most cases the creative scientific act comes before the operations which lead to the establishment of truth; together they make science.

"Many great experimenters in all fields of science have described how their ideas were determined in large part by unanalytical, visionary perceptions. Likewise, history shows that most specific scientific theories have emerged and have been formulated gradually from crude intuitive sketches.

If this fact is fully understood, we are apt to turn back upon the critics with some irritation and even with some readiness to make psychoanalytic interpretations of the critic rather than to answer him with logical arguments. For at this point we realize that the critics often *need* neatness, exactness, or precision and cannot tolerate its absence, that they select only those problems to work with that already satisfy this criterion, and that in effect their criticisms may amount to a rejection of the problems themselves. They may be criticizing not your methodology but you yourself for asking that particular question.

Scientists who need neatness and simplicity generally have sense enough to stay away from the humanistic and personal problems of human nature. Such a choice may indicate a preference for neatness over new knowledge of human nature, and this can be a way of avoiding the tough problems.

### LEVELS OF RELIABILITY OF KNOWLEDGE

There is some tendency to dichotomize knowledge into true or false, significant or nonsignificant, reliable or unreliable. It takes only a moment's thought to see that this is unwise. Reliability of knowledge is a matter of degree. So is truth and falsehood. And certainly so also is significance and pertinence.

If we know only one fact, that a coin tossed once has turned up heads, then the probability of turning up heads in a second toss is greater than one half, and any wise man would bet accordingly. This is so because the slight possibility of the coin being lopsided has been raised by the one bit of knowledge.

Knight Dunlap long ago showed that people who were

---

In this light, the first steps in the recognition of patterns or in the development of new concepts are more akin to artistic awareness than to what is commonly regarded as the 'scientific method.' " (R. Dubos, *The Dreams of Reason* [Columbia University Press, 1961], pp. 122-123.)

asked to guess which of two slightly different weights was heavier, would guess correctly more often than chance, even though they had no conscious confidence at all in their judgments. Consciously they felt that they were making pure guesses. Other researches have extended this kind of finding to group guessing. The mean of ten people guessing blindly (i.e., without subjective confidence) is apt to be closer to the true mean than will be the mean of five people guessing blindly.

The history of medicine—pharmacology in particular—demonstrates again and again that it pays to take seriously the beliefs of primitive tribesmen, for example, in the therapeutic powers of some herb or bark, even when their explanations are weird or can be proved false. A confused glimmer of the truth is possible from only vaguely understood learning experiences. And so in this realm as in others we give some credence, if only a little, to the expert opinion, to the hunch of the experienced clinician, to the educated guess. When we have no reliable facts to go on, we will turn for guidance to the best that's available.

All of us are used to this—when we deal with surgeons, psychiatrists, lawyers, etc. Especially is this so when we are forced to make decisions in the absence of satisfactory knowledge. But Polanyi (60, 61, 62), Northrop (59), Kuhn (30), and others have shown that something of the sort is also true in the strategy and tactics of the scientist himself. Creative persons have often reported their reliance on hunches, dreams, intuitions, blind guessing, and gambling in the early stages of the creative process. Indeed, we could almost define the creative scientist in that way—as the creative mathematician is already defined—i.e., as one who reaches the truth without knowing why or how. He just "feels" something to be correct and then proceeds *post hoc* to check his feeling by careful research. The choice of hypothesis to test, the choice of this rather than that problem to invest oneself in, is proved correct or incorrect only *after* the fact. We may judge him correct because of the facts that he has gathered, but he himself did not have these facts to base his confidence on. Indeed the facts are the consequence of his "unfounded" self-confidence, not the cause of it. We call a scientist "talented" for just this reason, that he is often right *in spite of* insufficient evidence. The lay picture of "the scientist" as one who keeps his mouth shut until he is sure of his facts is quite incorrect, at least for talented, "break-through" scientists. Polanyi rightly speaks of faith, connoisseurship, courage, self-confidence, and boldness in gambling as intrinsic to the nature of the trail-blazing theorist or researcher, as defining characteristics, not as accidental, fortuitous, or expendable.

And this can also be stated in terms of probabilities. The bold and productive scientist must be able to be comfortable with low probabilities. He must take them seriously as the clues to what he ought to do and the directions in which he ought to go. He must be sensitive to them and be guided by them. At least he must regard them as scientifically "real" and therefore worthy of his attention as a scientist.

It is both useful and correct to consider as falling within the definition of knowledge all "protoknowledge," so long as its probability of being correct is greater than chance. This usage would imply then a hierarchy of stages or levels or degrees of knowledge, ranging downward in degree of reliability to expert guesses, hunches and intuitions, tentative conclusions based on insufficient cases or upon crude methods, etc. Knowledge is then seen as more reliable or less reliable but still knowledge so long as its probability is greater than chance. The word "empirical" then gets used as the physician uses it, i.e., to describe an inchoate, apperceptive mass made up of thousands of experiences of "trying out" remedies on himself as well as upon his patients, of accepting common sense remedies tentatively, of judging face plausibility, etc.

This adds up to the tacit knowledge accumulated by the "experienced" physician. Hardly anything he knows has been adequately proved.

### THE SCIENTIST AS EXPLORER

The originator is to some extent more attracted to the complex rather than to the simple or easy, to the mysterious and unknown rather than to the known. What challenges him is that which he does *not* know. What fun, he feels, is there in a puzzle whose solution he knows? A known puzzle is no puzzle. It is the *not* knowing that fascinates him and that sets him into motion. For him the mystery "calls for" solving. It has "demand character." It beckons, attracts, and seduces.

The feeling of the scientific originator is that of a first explorer of an unknown wilderness, an unknown river or a strange mountain pass. He doesn't really know where he is going. He has no maps, no predecessors, no guides, no experienced helpers, few hints or orientation points. Every step he takes is a hypothesis, as likely to be a mistake as not.

And yet the word "mistake" hardly applies to a scout. A blind alley explored is no longer an unexplored blind alley. No one else need ever explore it. Something has been learned. If presented with a choice between a left and a right fork in the river, and having tried the left fork and found it to be a dead end, he doesn't consider that his choice was a "mistake" or an error. Certainly he would feel no guilt or regret and would look with astonishment upon someone who upbraided him for having made a choice without evidence or for moving ahead without being sure. He might then point out that upon such principles and with such rules no wilderness could *ever* be explored and that such principles were useful in re-exploring but not in exploring for the first time.

In a word, the rules, principles or laws of the explorer or

the scout are different from the rules suitable for later settlers simply because the tasks are different. What is functionally suitable for one is not suitable for the other. The beginning stages of knowledge should not be judged by the criteria derived from "final" knowledge.

## THE EMPIRICAL ATTITUDE

One trouble with defining science in terms of its highest reaches and ultimate skills is that it makes science and the scientific spirit inaccessible to most people. Stressing its technology and showing off its most esoteric abstractions make it look far more difficult than it really is. It comes to be seen as a matter for the expert, something done by a certain kind of highly trained professional and by nobody else. In effect this kind of science, after dividing the world into scientists and nonscientists, says to the nonscientists, "This is none of your business! Stay out! Leave it to us experts. Trust us!"

It is certainly true that the sciences of the impersonal, which are also our oldest sciences, have reached a high level of abstraction and that their technology is in fact a matter for trained experts. (I won't say "most advanced" sciences because this implies that all sciences can be ranked in a single scale, which is not true.) But it is equally true that the psychological and social or even the life sciences are far from being as complex, as abstract, or as technologized. There is still plenty of room for the amateur—many simple questions yet to be asked, many nooks and corners to be probed for the first time. In its beginnings, science is easy.

But my main point is more radical. If we define science in terms of its beginnings and its simplest levels rather than in terms of its highest and most complex levels, then science is simply looking at things for yourself rather than trusting to the a priori or to authority of any kind. It is this empirical attitude that I claim can and should be taught to all human beings, including young children. Look for yourself! Let's see how it works! Is that claim correct? How correct? Such as these, I believe, are the fundamental scientific questions and methods of science. And it follows that checking for yourself by going into the back yard and looking with your own eyes is more truly empirical and therefore more "scientific" than looking up the answer in Aristotle or, for that matter, in a textbook of science. It follows also that a child can be "scientific" watching an anthill and so can a housewife comparing the virtues of various soaps by trying them out in her basement.

The empirical attitude is a matter of degree rather than an all-or-none skill acquired all at once in a single moment when you get a Ph.D and that you can only then practice. This attitude can therefore be cultivated and improved bit by bit. And when phrased in this way—keeping in touch with reality, keeping your eyes open—it becomes almost a defining characteristic of humanness itself. Helping people to become more empirical is one way of improving their knowing and their knowledge. It helps their "reality testing," to use the psychoanalytic word. That is, it helps people to distinguish facts from wishes, from hopes, or from fears. And it also should help toward improvement of what I might call "psyche testing," truer knowledge of one's subjective world. It is necessary to know when one is wishing or hoping or fearing and whose wishes they are.

In a word, scientists are not a different species. They share with others the characteristic of curiosity, the desire and even the need to understand, to prefer seeing to being blind, and to prefer more reliable to less reliable knowledge. The specialized abilities of the professional scientist are intensifications of these general human qualities. Every normal person, even every child, is a simple, undeveloped, amateur scientist who can in principle be taught to be more sophisticated, more skilled, more advanced. A humanistic view of science and of scientists would certainly suggest such a domestication and democratization of the empirical attitude.

Such a recommendation flows even more strongly from a transhuman or transcendental view of science and scientists. The process of acquiring knowledge (at all its levels) and the contemplation and enjoyment of it is turning out to be one of the richest sources of esthetic raptures, of semireligious ecstasies, of experiences of awe and mystery. Such emotional experiences are among the ultimate joys of living. Orthodox desacralizing science has for various reasons tried to purge itself of these transcendent experiences. Such purging, far from being necessary in order to safeguard the purity of science, is instead a deprivation and a removal from science of its human necessities. It is almost like saying that science need not or cannot be enjoyed.

Such experiences of joy are necessary not only because they bring people into science and keep them there, but also because these esthetic joys may also be cognitive signs, like signal rockets that go off to tell us we have found something important (*63*). It is in the peak experiences that Being-cognition (*43, 44, 46*) is most likely to take place. In such moments we are perhaps most able to see into the heart of things.

# 14

## The Desacralization and the Resacralization of Science[1]

The nonscientists, the poets, the religious, the artists, and ordinary people in general may have a point in their fear, and even hatred of what they see as science. They often feel it to be a threat to everything that they hold marvelous and sacred, to everything beautiful, sublime, valuable, and awe-inspiring. They sometimes see it as a contaminator, a spoiler, a reducer, that makes life bleak and mechanical, robs it of color and joy, and imposes on it a spurious certainty. Look into the mind of the average high school student and this is the picture you see (54). The girls will often shudder at the thought of marrying a scientist, as if he were some sort of respectable monster. Even when we resolve some of the misinterpretations in the layman's mind, such as his confounding the scientist with the technologist, his inability to differentiate between the "revolution scientist" and the "normal scientist" or between the physical and the social sciences, some justified complaint is left. This "need to desacralize as a defense" has, so far as I know, not been discussed by the scientists themselves.

[1] By this term I mean removal or destruction of either emotion or ceremony. Here I follow Eliade's usage (18) in spite of etymological difficulties which have been pointed out to me by S. Joseph Peake. "Desanctification" would be more correct in referring to feelings; "desacralization" refers more to ceremonies and rites. I shall use the latter word to cover both feelings and ceremonies.

Briefly put, it appears to me that science and everything scientific can be and often is used as a tool in the service of a distorted, narrowed, humorless, de-eroticized, de-emotionalized, desacralized and desanctified *Weltanschauung*. This desacralization can be used as a defense against being flooded by emotion, especially the emotions of humility, reverence, mystery, wonder, and awe (*18, 48*).

I think I can best make my meaning clear by an example from my experiences thirty years ago in medical school. I didn't consciously realize it then, but in retrospect it seems clear that our professors were almost deliberately trying to harden us, to teach us to confront death, pain, and disease in a "cool," unemotional manner. The first operation I ever saw was almost a representative example of the effort to desacralize, i.e., to remove the sense of awe, privacy, fear, and shyness before the sacred and of humility before the tremendous. A woman's breast was to be amputated with an electrical scalpel that cut by burning through. As a delicious aroma of grilling steak filled the air, the surgeon made carelessly "cool" and casual remarks about the pattern of his cutting, paying no attention to the freshmen rushing out in distress, and finally tossing this object through the air onto the counter where it landed with a plop. It had changed from a sacred object to a discarded lump of fat. There were, of course, no tears, prayers, rituals, or ceremonies of any kind, as there would certainly have been in most preliterate societies (*18*). This was all handled in a purely technological fashion—emotionless, calm, even with a slight tinge of swagger.

The atmosphere was about the same when I was introduced —or rather *not* introduced—to the dead man I was to dissect. I had to find out for myself what his name was and that he had been a lumberman and was killed in a fight. And I had to learn to treat him as everyone else did, not as a dead person but without ceremony, as a "cadaver." So also for the several beautiful dogs I had to kill in my physiology classes when we had finished with our demonstrations and experiments.

The new medics themselves tried to make their deep feelings manageable and controllable by suppressing their fears, their compassion, their tender feelings, their awe before stark life and death, their tears as they all identified with the frightened patients. Since they were young men, they did it in adolescent ways, e.g., getting photographed while seated on a cadaver and eating a sandwich, casually pulling a human hand out of a brief case at the restaurant table, making standard medic jokes about the private recesses of the body, etc.

This counterphobic toughness, casualness, unemotionality and profaning (covering over their opposites) was apparently thought to be necessary, since tender emotions might interfere with the objectivity and fearlessness of the physician. (I myself have often wondered if this desacralizing and desanctifying was really necessary. It is at least possible that a more priestly and less engineerlike attitude might improve medical training —or at least not drive out the "softer" candidates.[2] Also we must now take issue with the implied assumption that emotion must be an enemy of truth and objectivity. Sometimes it is, and sometimes it is not.)

There are many other situations in which desacralizing can be seen more clearly as a defense. We are all acquainted with people who can't stand intimacy, honesty, defenselessness, those who get uneasy with close friendship, who can't love or be loved. Running away from this disturbing intimacy or beauty is a usual solution, or it can be "distanced," i.e., held at arm's length. Or finally it can be gutted, deprived of its disturbing quality, denatured. For instance, innocence can be redefined as stupidity, honesty can be called gullibility, candor

---

[2] It is *possible* that this kind of "tough" training is necessary for a surgeon. That is debatable. But for a psychotherapist? for an "interpersonal knower" through caring and love? Clearly it is an *anti*psychological training!

becomes lack of common sense, and generosity is labeled soft-headedness. The former disturbs; the latter does not and can be dealt with. (Remember that there really is no way of "dealing with" great beauty or blinding truth or perfection—or with any of the ultimate Being-values; all we can do is contemplate, be delighted, be "amused," adore, etc.)

In an ongoing investigation of what I am calling "counter-values" (the fear or hatred of truth, goodness, beauty, perfection, order, aliveness, uniqueness, and the other Being-values), I am finding in general that these highest values tend to make the person more conscious of everything in himself that is the opposite of these values. Many young men feel more comfortable with a girl who isn't too pretty. The beautiful girl is apt to make him feel sloppy, gawky, stupid, unworthy, as if he were in the presence of some kind of royalty or deity. Desacralization can be a defense against this battering of self-esteem shaky enough to need defending.

Just as obvious and just as well known to the clinician is the inability of some men to have sexual intercourse with a good or beautiful woman unless they degrade her first—or at least make her not a goddess. It is difficult for the man who identifies his role in the sexual act with a dirty act of intrusion or of domination to do this to a goddess or madonna or priestess—to a sacred, awesome mother. So he must drag her down from her pedestal above the world into the world of dirty human beings by making himself master, perhaps in a gratuitously sadistic way, or by reminding himself that she defecates and sweats and urinates or that she can be bought, etc. Then he need no longer respect her; he is freed from feeling awed, tender, worshipful, profane, or unworthy, from feeling clumsy and inadequate like a frightened little boy.

Less studied by the dynamic psychologists but probably as frequent a phenomenon is the symbolic castration of the male by his female. Certainly this is known to occur widely in our society at least, but it is usually given either a straight socio-logical or else a straight Freudian explanation. Quite as prob-able, I think, is the possibility that "castration" may also be for the sake of desacralizing and desanctifying the male, that Xan-thippe is also fighting against being flooded and overwhelmed by her great respect for and awe of her Socrates.

Also what frequently passes for "explanation" is not so much an effort to understand or to communicate understand-ing or to enrich it as it is an effort to abort awe, marvel, and wonder. The child who is thrilled by a rainbow may be told in a slightly scornful and debunking way, "Oh, that's only the scattering of white light into colors by droplets acting like prisms." This can be a devaluation of the experience in a sort of one-upmanship that laughs at the child and his naïveté. And it can have the effect of aborting the experience so that it is less likely to come again or to be openly expressed or to be taken seriously. It can have the effect of taking the awe and wonder out of life. I have found this to be true for peak-experiences. They are easily and often "explained away" rather than really explained. One friend of mine, during post-surgical relief and contemplation, had a great illumination in the classical style, profound and shaking. When I got over being impressed with his revelation, I bethought myself of the wonderful research possibilities that this experience opened up. I asked the surgeon if other patients had such visions after surgery. He said casually, "Oh, yes! Demerol, you know."

Of course such "explanations" explain nothing about the content of the experience itself any more than a trigger ex-plains the effects of an explosion. And then these explanations that achieve nothing must themselves be understood and ex-plained.

So also for the reductive effort and the "nothing but" atti-tude, e.g.: "A human being is really nothing but $24 worth of chemicals"; "A kiss is the juxtaposing of the upper ends of two gastrointestinal tracts"; "A man is what he eats"; "Love is the overestimation of the differences between your girl and all other girls." I've chosen these adolescent-boy examples deliberately because this is where I believe the use of desacralization as a defense is at its height. These boys trying to be tough or "cool" or "grown-up" typically have to fight their awe, humility, love, tenderness, and compassion, their sense of miracle and marvel. They do this by dragging the "high" down to the "low," where they feel that they themselves are. These "idealistic" youngsters keep busily fighting against their impulses to do homage by trying to desacralize and profane everything, as "normal" adults do.

The general-atomistic techniques of dissection, etc. may also be used for this same purpose. One can avoid feeling stunned, unworthy, or ignorant before, let us say, a beautiful flower or insect or poem simply by taking it apart and feeling masterful again. So also for classifying, taxonomizing, categorizing, rubricizing in general. These, too, are ways of making awesome things mundane, secular, manageable, everyday. Any form of abstracting that avoids a comprehensive wholeness may serve this same purpose.

So the question must be asked: is it in the intrinsic nature of science or knowledge that it must desacralize? Or is it possible to include in the realm of reality the mysterious, the awe-inspiring, the B-humorous (44), the emotionally shaking, the beautiful, the sacred? And if they be conceded to exist, how can we get to know them?

Laymen are often wrong when they feel that the scientist is necessarily desacralizing life. They misunderstand the attitude with which the best scientists approach their work. The "unitive" aspect of this attitude (perceiving simultaneously the sacred and the profane) is too easily overlooked, especially since most scientists are shy about expressing it.

The truth is that the really good scientist often *does* approach his work with love, devotion, and self-abnegation, as if he were entering into a holy of holies. His self-forgetfulness can certainly be called a transcendence of the ego. His absolute morality of honesty and total truth can certainly be called a "religious" attitude, and his occasional thrill or peak-experience, the occasional shudder of awe, of humility and smallness before the great mysteries he deals with—all these can be called sacred (*18, 48*). This does not happen often, but it does happen and sometimes under circumstances difficult for the layman to identify.

It is easy to elicit such secret attitudes from some scientists, if only you assume that they exist and take them seriously. If science could discard this unnecessary "taboo on tenderness," it would be less misunderstood and within its own precincts would find less need for desacralizing and making merely profane.

We can also learn much from self-actualizing, highly healthy people. They have higher ceilings. They can see further. And they can see in a more inclusive and integrating way. They teach us that there is no real opposition between caution and courage, between action and contemplation, between vigor and speculation, between tough-mindedness and tender-mindedness, between seriousness and (Olympian) humor. These are all human qualities, and they are all useful in science. In these people there is no need to deny reality to experiences of transcendence or to regard such experiences as "unscientific" or anti-intellectual. That is, such people feel no need to deny their deeper feelings. Indeed, it is my impression that, if anything, they tend rather to enjoy such experiences.

## THE GOOD-HUMORED SCIENTIST

Another kind of criticism of official science and scientists comes from their tendency to place too great faith in their abstractions and to be too certain of them. In this way they also are likely to lose their sense of humor, their skepticism, their humility, and that becoming consciousness of deeper ignorance that forbids *hubris*. This criticism is especially apt in the psychological and social sciences. It is certainly true that physical scientists can plume themselves on their remarkable achievements and their mastery of objects and inanimate nature. But what have psychologists to be proud of? How much do they really know that is helpful to human concerns? Orthodox science has been a failure in all the human and social realms.[3] (I pass by the question of the so-called "success" that results in atom bombs that are then given into the charge of psychologically and socially primitive individuals and societies. Is it not dangerous for the right arm of science to grow to giant proportions while the left arm lags so far behind in its growth?)

If I am right, it would certainly be wise and gracious of scientists—it would even be "scientific" in the truest sense—if they denied themselves the pleasures of "methodolatry," i.e., if they refused to become arrogant, blustering, and smug. The graces that would save them are rather such traits as modesty, the ability to laugh at themselves, to live with ambiguity, the constant awareness of the possibility of multiple theories for any set of facts, the acute consciousness of the intrinsic limits of language and of abstraction and of science itself, acknowledgement of the primacy of experiences, of facts, of description over all theories, a fear of living too long in the thin upper air of theories before coming back to the earthy facts. Finally I would add that experiential knowledge of the unconscious and preconscious determinants of one's own scientific work is the greatest humility producer of all.

---

[3] We *do* have much useful knowledge of persons and societies, but I would maintain that much of it comes from heterodox sources, i.e., from humanistic science rather than from mechanistic science.

A revealing comparison may be made with the tendency of most authoritarian characters to be unable to wait and hold judgment in abeyance. It is the widespread clinical impression —the experimental data are still ambiguous—that they just can't stand waiting. It makes them tense and anxious. And they tend to leap prematurely to a conclusion, *any* conclusion, rather than remain in this, for them, state of emotional purgatory. Not only this, but once they are committed to a conclusion, they also tend to hang on to it too long, even in the face of contradictory information.

The more sagacious and Olympian, the more amused and ironic contemplator is aware that theories in science have been far more temporary than they expected to be, and they may therefore feel that it is just as silly to be totally "loyal" to the laws of Newton as to the house of the Hohenzollerns.

This more tentative attitude can be based firmly on empirical grounds. If one remains close to the world of concrete facts, it is impossible to deny their multiplicity, their contradictions, their ambiguity. One becomes aware of the relativity of our knowledge of this world of facts, relativity to the century, the culture, the class and caste, the personal character of the observer. It is so easy to feel certain and yet to be mistaken.[4]

To sail into the teeth of such opposing forces, especially when one is aware of them, is itself a sign of courage and even nobility. It should make scientists feel fortunate, pleased with their lives, that they have sworn devotion to the eternal ques-

---

[4] "All science is only a make-shift, a means to an end which is never attained . . . all description is postponed till we know the whole, but then science itself will be cast aside. But unconsidered expressions of our delight which any natural object draws from us are something complete and final in themselves, since all nature is to be regarded as it concerns man; and who knows how near to absolute truth such unconscious affirmations may come? . . . *We shall see but little if we require to understand what we see.* How few things can a man measure with the tape of his understanding." (Thoreau)

tions that are certainly worthy of the highest human efforts.

One way in which it is possible to be empirical, to work at advancing knowledge, to value this knowledge greatly, and yet also to be realistic about the paucity and unreliability of human knowledge is to be detached about it, godlike, skeptically amused and affectionate, ironical, tolerant, and wondering. Laughing (in the right way) is one good way of handling an insoluble problem and of simultaneously retaining the strength to keep working at it. A sense of humor can be an excellent solution to the existential problem of being humble and yet also being proud, arrogant, and strong (enough to work at great tasks). In this way we can simultaneously be aware of what we know about rockets and antibiotics and what we *don't* know about war and peace, prejudice, or greed.

These are all forms of contemplation of the confusion of what exists and are the mild enjoyments that permit us to go on trying persistently to unravel the confusion a little more without losing heart. One can love science even though it is not perfect, just as one can love one's wife even though she is not perfect. And, fortunately, for just a moment and as an unexpected and undeserved reward they sometimes *do* become perfect and take our breath away.

Such an attitude helps to transcend certain other problems. One important one is the covert identification of a science with completed knowledge. It has been my experience to hear psychologists sneered at by physicists, for example, because they don't know much and because what they do know is not highly abstracted and mathematized. "Do you call *that* a science?" they ask, with the implication that science is knowing rather than questioning. Thus the rear-echelon soldier sneers at the front-light fighter for being dirty, and the inheritor of wealth sneers at the sweaty one who is earning it. The psychologist knows that there are two hierarchies of esteem in science (not just one). One is the hierarchy of well organized knowledge; the other is the hierarchy of importance of the questions one chooses to work with. It is the ones that choose to work with the crucial, unsolved, human questions who have taken on their shoulders the fate of mankind.

### NAIVE WONDER, SCIENCE, AND SOPHISTICATED WONDER

Most of the definitions of science, especially those written by nonscientists, are ultimately inaccurate. Science is too often presented as a kind of functionally autonomous enterprise that cannot really make sense to the outsider. For instance, if you call it a "growing corpus of information" or a "system of concepts operationally defined," laymen might wonder why people should dedicate their lives to such unexciting ends. Such descriptions of the end products of scientific work or of science as a social institution or, for that matter, any talk of science rather than of scientists tends to leave out all the fun, the passion, the excitement, the triumph, the disappointment, the emotional and the conative, not to mention the "esthetic," the "religious," or the "philosophical" turmoil of the scientist's life. A fair parallel would be reading about the rules of chess, its history, studying individual games, etc. All this might give no answer at all to the question, "Why do people play chess?" If you know nothing about their emotions, their motivations and satisfactions, they will remain forever inscrutable, as gamblers are to nongamblers.

I believe it is possible for nonscientists to get some feeling for the scientist's life via some understanding of his goals and satisfactions, since these psychologically real satisfactions are shared to an extent by everyone.

In my investigations of peak-experiences I learned that these experiences are much more alike than the triggers that set them off. I felt much closer to women, for instance, after I discovered that they describe their moments of highest happiness in about the same way that men do, even though they are "turned on" by situations that leave men untouched. So far as the inner lives of individual scientists are concerned, these peak-experiences are much like those set off in the poets by poetry, etc. For my part, I think that I have got more "poetical" experiences from my own and others' researches than I have from poetry. I have got more "religious" experiences from reading scientific journals than I have from reading "sacred books." The thrills of creating something beautiful come to me via my experiments, my explorations, my theoretical work rather than from painting or composing music or dancing. Science can be a way of marrying with that which you love, with that which fascinates you and with whose mystery you would love to spend your life.

But to continue with the parallel, you may spend a lifetime getting to know more and more about your subject and wind up, after fifty years of learning, feeling even more overwhelmed with its mystery and solving the whole business by being amused with it. Of course, this is now an enriched and "higher" mystery and wonder, different from the blank mystification of the ignorant. The two processes seem to go on simultaneously and in parallel, i.e., knowing more and more and feeling the mystery more and more. At least this is what happens in our paragons and our sages, our best scientists, the ones who remain integrated human beings rather than becoming hemiplegic specialists. And these are the scientists who can be understood by poets and who in turn can see the poet as a kind of collaborator. Science *can* be the "poetry of the intellect," as L. Durrell has put it. This exploration of the secret inner life of good scientists can be a foundation for a kind of ecumenical movement that will bring together scientists, artists, "religious" people, humanists, and all other serious people.

Many people still think that scientific study or detailed knowing is the opposite and the contradiction of the sense of mystery.[5] But this need not be the case. Studying the mystery does not necessarily profane it. Indeed, this is the best way toward greater respect, richer understanding, and greater sacralization and sanctification at a much higher level of richness. Remember that it has always been our wisest men who were most simple, least arrogant, and most "amused."

Knowing more about trees and how they work can make them more beautiful. The tree that I look at and admire is now *more* a miracle because I know a little botany. If I knew still more about the details of its functioning, this knowledge could make the tree still more miraculous and beautiful. For instance, one of the most profound esthetic experiences of my life came to me long ago in a histology class. Here I had been studying the physiology, the chemistry, and the physics of the kidney. The more I learned, the more I marveled at its beautiful and unbelievable intricacy and simplicity and its functionally perfect form. Its form followed its function far more sculpturally than anything Greenough (*Form and Function: Remarks on Art* [Univ. of California Press, 1947]) had ever dreamed of. The evolution of the kidney, as the comparative embryologists had learned it, was for me still another marvel so improbable that it could never have been anticipated a priori. It was at this point, after studying, learning, and knowing, that I looked at a perfectly stained slide under the micro-

[5] When I heard the learn'd astronomer,
When the proofs, the figures, were ranged in columns before me,
When I was shown the charts and diagrams, to add, divide, and measure them,
When I sitting heard the astronomer where he lectured with much applause in the lecture room,
How soon unaccountable I became tired and sick,
Till rising and gliding out I wander'd off by myself,
In the mystical moist night-air, and from time to time,
Look'd up in perfect silence at the stars.

—WALT WHITMAN

scope and had an experience of beauty so great that I remember it thirty-five years later.

This is what nonscientists don't know, and this is what scientists are too bashful to talk about publicly, at least until they grow old enough to become shameless. Science at its highest level is ultimately the organization of, the systematic pursuit of, and the enjoyment of wonder, awe, and mystery. The greatest rewards that the scientist can have are such peak-experiences and B-cognitions as these. But these experiences can equally be called religious experiences, poetic experiences, or philosophical experiences. Science can be the religion of the nonreligious, the poetry of the nonpoet, the art of the man who cannot paint, the humor of the serious man, and the love-making of the inhibited and shy man. Not only does science begin in wonder; it also ends in wonder.

# Bibliography

1. ALLPORT, G. W. "The General and the Unique in Psychological Science," *Journal of Personality,* XXX (1962), 405–422.
2. ALLPORT, G. W., Ed. *Letters From Jenny.* New York: Harcourt, Brace & World, 1965.
3. Anonymous. *Journal of Humanistic Psychology,* I (1961), 101–102.
4. ASCH, S. "Studies of Independence and Conformity, Part I," *Psychological Monographs,* LXX (1956). (Whole No. 416.)
5. BAKAN, D. "The Mystery-Mastery Complex in Contemporary Psychology," *American Psychologist,* XX (1965), 186–191.
6. BERTALANFFY, L. V. *Modern Theories of Development.* New York: Oxford Univ. Press, 1933.
7. BERTALANFFY, L. V. *Problems of Life.* New York: Wiley, 1952.
8. BRIDGMAN, P. W. *The Way Things Are.* Cambridge, Mass.: Harvard Univ. Press, 1959.
9. BRONOWSKI, J. *The Common Sense of Science.* London: Heinemann, 1951.
10. BRONOWSKI, J. *Science and Human Values.* New York: Harper & Row, 1956.
11. BRONOWSKI, J. "The Values of Science," in *New Knowledge in Human Values,* ed. A. H. Maslow, New York: Harper & Row, 1959.
12. BUBER, M. *I and Thou.* New York: Scribner, 1958.
13. CRAIG, R., Characteristics of creativeness and self-actualization. To be published.

14. CRUTCHFIELD, R. "Conformity and Character," *American Psychologist,* X (1955), 191–198.
15. DALTON, M. "Preconceptions and Methods in Men who Manage," in *Sociologists At Work,* ed. P. Hammond. New York: Basic Books, 1964.
16. DUBOS, R. *The Dreams of Reason.* New York: Columbia Univ. Press, 1961.
17. EDDINGTON, A. *The Philosophy of Physical Science.* Ann Arbor: Univ. of Michigan Press., 1939.
18. ELIADE, M. *The Sacred and The Profane.* New York: Harper & Row, 1961.
19. FARRINGTON, B. *Greek Science.* London: Penguin Books, 1949.
20. FRIEDENBERG, E. Z. "Why Students Leave Science," *Commentary,* XXXII (1961), 144–155.
21. GENDLIN, E. *Experiencing and the Creation of Meaning.* New York: Free Press, 1962.
22. GOLDSTEIN, K. *The Organism.* New York: American Book Co., 1939.
23. HENLE, M., Ed. *Documents of Gestalt Psychology.* Berkeley: Univ. of California Press, 1961.
24. HOOK, S., Ed. *Psychoanalysis, Scientific Method & Philosophy.* New York: New York Univ. Press, 1959.
25. HUXLEY, A. *Literature and Science.* New York: Harper & Row, 1963.
26. KRUTCH, J. W. *Human Nature and the Human Condition.* New York: Random House, 1959.
27. KUBIE, L. S. "The Forgotten Man of Education," *Harvard Alumni Bulletin,* LVI: 8 (1953–1954), 349–353.
28. KUBIE, L. "Some Unsolved Problems of the Scientific Career," *American Scientist,* XLI (1953), 596–613; XLII (1954), 104–112.
29. KUENZLI, A., Ed. *The Phenomenological Problem.* New York: Harper & Row, 1959.
30. KUHN, T. S. *The Structure of Scientific Revolutions.* Chicago: Univ. of Chicago Press, 1962.
31. LEWIN, K. *A Dynamic Theory of Personality.* New York: McGraw-Hill, 1935.
32. MCCURDY, H. G. *Personality & Science.* New York: Van Nostrand, 1965.

33. MASLOW, A. H. "The Influence of Familiarization on Preferences," *Journal of Experimental Psychology*, XXI (1937), 162–180.
34. MASLOW, A. H., with Bela Mittelmann. *Principles of Abnormal Psychology: The Dynamics of Psychic Illness.* New York: Harper & Bros., 1941.
35. MASLOW, A. H. "The Authoritarian Character Structure," *Journal of Social Psychology*, XVIII (1943), 401–411.
36. MASLOW, A. H. "A Suggested Improvement in Semantic Usage," *Psychological Review*, LII (1945), 239–240.
37. MASLOW, A. H. "Experimentalizing the Clinical Method," *Journal of Clinical Psychology*, I (1945), 241–243.
38. MASLOW, A. H. *Motivation and Personality.* New York: Harper & Bros., 1954.
39. MASLOW, A. H. "Two Kinds of Cognition and Their Integration," *General Semantics Bulletin*, Nos. 20 & 21 (1957), 17–22.
40. MASLOW, A. H., Ed. *New Knowledge in Human Values.* New York: Harper & Bros., 1959.
41. MASLOW, A. H., with H. Rand & S. Newman. "Some Parallels between the Dominance and Sexual Behavior of Monkeys and the Fantasies of Patients in Psychotherapy," *Journal of Nervous & Mental Disease*, CXXXI (1960), 202–212.
42. MASLOW, A. H. "Comments on Skinner's Attitude to Science," *Daedalus*, XC (1961), 572–573.
43. MASLOW, A. H. *Toward a Psychology of Being.* New York: Van Nostrand, 1962.
44. MASLOW, A. H. "Notes on Being-Psychology," *Journal Humanistic Psychology*, II (1962), 47–71.
45. MASLOW, A. H. "The Creative Attitude," *The Structurist*, III (1963), 4–10. Repr. separately by *Psychosynthesis Foundation* (1963).
46. MASLOW, A. H. "Fusions of Facts and Values," *American Journal of Psychoanalysis*, XXIII (1963), 117–131.
47. MASLOW, A. H. "Notes on Innocent Cognition," in *Gegenwartsprobleme der Entwicklungspsychologie: Festschrift für Charlotte Buhler*, ed. L. Schenk-Danzinger & H. Thomae. Göttingen: Verlag für Psychologie, 1963.
48. MASLOW, A. H. *Religions, Values and Peak-experiences.* Columbus, Ohio: Ohio State Univ. Press, 1964.

49. MASLOW, A. H., with L. Gross. "Synergy in Society and in the Individual," *Journal of Individual Psychology,* XX (1964), 153–164.
50. MASLOW, A. H. "Criteria for Judging Needs to be Instinctoid," in *Human Motivation: A Symposium,* ed. M. R. Jones. Lincoln, Nebraska: Univ. of Nebraska Press, 1965.
51. MASLOW, A. H. *Eupsychian Management: A Journal.* Homewood, Illinois: Irwin-Dorsey, 1965.
52. MASLOW, A. H. "Isomorphic Interrelationships Between Knower and Known," in *Sign, Image, Symbol,* ed. G. Kepes. New York: Braziller, 1966.
53. MATSON, F. *The Broken Image.* New York: Braziller, 1964.
54. MEAD, M., and R. Metraux. "Image of the Scientist among High School Students," *Science,* CXXVI (1957), 384–390.
55. MORANT, R., and A. H. Maslow. "Art Judgment and the Judgment of Others,"*Journal of Clinical Psychology,* XXI (1965), 389–391.
56. NAMECHE, G. "Two Pictures of Man," *Journal of Humanistic Psychology,* I (1961), 70–88.
57. NAMECHE, G., and Morant, R. B. "Esthetic Judgment and Person Perception." Unpubl. MS.
58. NORTHROP, F. C. S. *The Meeting of East and West.* New York: Macmillan, 1946.
59. NORTHROP, F. C. S. *The Logic of the Sciences and the Humanities.* New York: Macmillan, 1947.
60. POLANYI, M. *Personal Knowledge.* Chicago: Univ. of Chicago Press, 1958.
61. POLANYI, M. *The Study of Man.* Chicago: Univ. of Chicago Press, 1959.
62. POLANYI, M. *Science, Faith and Society.* Chicago: Univ. of Chicago Press, 1964.
63. PRABHU, P. H. "The State of Psychology as a Science Today," *Indian Psychological Review,* I (1964), 1–11.
64. ROE, A. *The Making of a Scientist.* New York: Dodd, Mead, 1952.
65. ROGERS, C. "Toward a Science of the Person," *Journal of Humanistic Psychology,* II (1963), 72–92.
66. ROGERS, C. "Some Thoughts Regarding the Current Philosophy of the Behavioral Sciences." Unpubl. MS.
67. SARGENT, H. "Intrapsychic Change: Methodological Problems

in Psychotherapy Research," *Psychiatry,* XXIV (1961), 93–108.

68. SIU, R. G. H. *The Tao of Science.* New York: Wiley, 1957.
69. SOROKIN, P. *Fads & Foibles in Modern Sociology and Related Sciences.* Chicago: Regnery, 1956.
70. STANDEN, A. *Science Is a Sacred Cow.* New York: Dutton, 1950.
71. TOLMAN, E. C. *Purposive Behavior in Animals and Men.* New York: Century, 1932.
72. TORRANCE, E. P. *Guiding Creative Talent.* Englewood Cliffs, N.J.: Prentice-Hall, 1962.
73. VAN KAAM, A. "Phenomenal Analysis: Exemplified by a Study of the Experience of 'really feeling understood,' " *Journal of Individual Psychology,* XV (1959), 66–72.
74. WANN, T. W., Ed, *Behaviorism and Phenomenology.* Chicago: University of Chicago Press, 1964. (Contributors: S. Koch, R. B. MacLeod, N. Malcolm, C. R. Rogers, M. Scriven, B. F. Skinner)
75. WATSON, D. L. *Scientists Are Human.* London: Watts and Co., 1938.
76. WATSON, D. L. *The Study of Human Nature.* Antioch, Ohio: Antioch Press, 1953.
77. WEISSKOPF, E. "Some Comments Concerning the Role of Education in the 'creation of creation,' " *Journal of Educational Psychology,* XLII (1951), 185–189.
78. WHITEHEAD, A. N. *Science and the Modern World.* New York: Macmillan, 1948.
79. WIENPAHL, P. *The Matter of Zen.* New York: New York Univ. Press, 1964.
80. WILSON, C. *Beyond the Outsider.* London: Arthur Barker, Ltd., 1964.
81. WINTHROP, H. "Scientism in Psychology," *Journal of Individual Psychology,* XV (1959), 112–120.
82. WOLFF, K. "Surrender as a Response to Our Crisis," *Journal of Humanistic Psychology,* II (1962), 16–30.

# Index

Abstraction: desacralizing tendency in, 143; experience and, 66-71, 74-75; limits of, 145; as meaning, 84-94; mechanistic, 135, 147

Acting out, 19, 37

Addiction, psychotherapy and, 58-61

Adler, Alfred, *xiv*, 8, 124

Adolescence, 36-37, 143

Alcoholics Anonymous, 46, 58

Alienation, 104, 105, 106-107; knowledge and, 49-52; values and, 140-141

Allport-Vernon-Lindzey test, 123

Altruism, *x*, 15

Ambiguity, 27, 31

Animals, *ix*, 7, 13, 40

Anthropology, objectivity and, 115-116

Anti-intellectualism, *xv-xvi*, 63

Anxiety. *See* Fear

Apollodorus, 5 *n.*

Aristotle, 9; influence of, 19, 69, 114, 119, 136

Asch, S., cited, 28

Ashton-Warner, Sylvia, quoted, 52

Art, 37, 149, 151; meaning and, 85, 87, 89-90; receptivity and, 97; style perception test, 62-64; *see also* Esthetics

Astronomy: empathy and, 19, 113; mechanistic tradition and, 9, 18, 102, 114

Atomism, *xiv*, 95; desacralizing tendency in, 143; dichotomizing, 34-35; in education, 63; psychology and, 3-4, 11; *see also* Reductiveness

Attentiveness, 20-21; knowledge and, 10-11, 12, 98-99, 106; Taoist, 96; *see also* Receptivity

Authority, 28, 36-37, 85 *n.*, 146

Baudelaire, Charles, quoted, 130 *n.*

Beauty, *xiv*, 15, 140, 141; *see also* Esthetics

Beethoven, Ludwig van, 90

Behavior: *ix-xii*, 59; compulsive-obsessive, 25-26; predictability and, 42-44; scientific, 20-22; *see also* *specific kinds of behavior, e.g., Contemplation*

Behaviorism, 47; mechanistic tradition of, *ix-xii*, 1-6, 13-16; objectivity of, 55-56, 75 *n.*

Being, psychology of, 91, 116; *see also* Experience; Reality

Being-Cognition, 116, 117, 137

Being-Love, 116-118

Being-Values, 43, 141

Bertalanffy, Ludwig von, *xv;* quoted, 3

Biology, *xv*, 3, 102; idiographic questions in, 9-10; receptivity and, 130 *n.*

Bohr, Niels, cited, 45 *n.*

Botany, 63

"Brainstorming," 54 *n.*

Bridgman, Percy, quoted, 57 *n.*

*Broken Image* (Matson), 2

Bronowski, Jacob, *xx,* 127

Buber, Martin, 50, 106

Castration, 141-142

Catholics, 61 *n.* 6

Causality, *xiv,* 3

Caution. *See* Fear

Certainty, 58, 68, 73, 82; humor and, 144-148, 149; pleasure in, 93; probability and, 131-134; *see also* Knowledge

Character disorders, 29

Chemistry, 9, 19, 76, 109, 150

Child psychology, 63

Classification: desacralizing tendency in, 143; empiricism and, 77; of experience, 54, 67; meaning and, 84, 87, 88; particularity and, 8-11; pathological, 29; theory and, 80-81; *see also* Rubricizing

Clinical psychology, 21, 48; origins of, 102; particularity and, 10-11; receptivity and, 97-98; values of, *xvi,* 94 *n.*

Cognition. *See* Knowledge

Communication: experience and, 58-59, 65; knowledge and, 45-47, 129-130; love and, 103; meaning and, 85-86, 87, 88-89, 90

Communists, 112-113

Compassion, 15, 36-37, 139-140

Comprehensiveness, 72-83, 84; *see also* Holism

Conditioning, 7, 13

Confidence, 55

Conformity, 28

Consciousness, *xiv,* 19, 106; *see also* Knowledge

Contemplation: desacralization of, 139-144; joy and, 137; order and, 147; scientific, 144; Taoist technique of, 96-97, 99-101

Control, 81, 107; personality and, 40-44; receptivity *versus,* 95-101; *see also* Domination; Self-control

Cooperativeness, 15

Copernicus, Nicholas, 17

Coping mechanisms, 22, 23

"Counter-values," 141

Courage, scientific, 18, 20-32, 122-123, 144, 146-147

Craig, Richard, on creativity, 38

Creativity, 15, 38, 40; fear of, 35-36; holistic perception and, 64; orthodoxy and, 31-32, 33, 34; scientific, 130 *n.,* 132-133, 134-137

Crutchfield, R., cited, 28

Curiosity, 15, 20-32

Darwin, Charles, 16-17

Death, contemplation and, 100

Defense mechanisms, 22-23, 24-26; cognitive, 26-30; desacralization and, 138-139, 140-144; in learning, 26-30; introspection and, 47; psychic, 16, 17-18; scientific, 33-39

Deficiency: as motivation, 22-23, 24-26; neurosis and, 124-125

Desacralization, 121, 138-151

Determinism, *xiv; see also* Mechanistic tradition

Development. *See* Growth

Dewey, John, *xi-xii*

Dialectic, 23 *n.,* 29, 34 *n.*

Dichotomization: of abstraction and experience, 86-87, 88; compulsive, 29; esthetic, 85 *n.*; integration versus, 34-35; of knowledge, 66, 67, 131; of religion and science, 119-121

Distance. *See* Alienation

Doctrine. *See* Orthodoxy

Domination: fear of, 36, 37, 42; sex as, 141-142

Dreams, interpretation of, 12

*Dreams of Reason, The* (Dubos), 130 *n.*

Dostoevsky, Fyodor, 86

Drug addicts, 58-61

Dubos, R., quoted, 130 *n.*

Dunlap, Knight, cited, 131

Durrell, L., quoted, 149

Eastman, Max, on Socialism, 70
Ecology, receptivity and, 98-99
Economics, *xiv,* 108
Eddington, Arthur Stanley, 100
Education: esthetic, 62-64; experience and, 60-64; immature views of, 37; scientific, 48-49, 118, 139-140, 142
Egotism, 28, 52, 53
Eliade, M., cited, 138 *n.*
Eliot, T. S., quoted, 90 *n.*
Ellison, Ralph, quoted, 126-127
Embryology, *xv,* 9, 150
Emotion, 31, 38; anti-intellectualism and, 63; desacralization defense against, 139-144; experience of, 45 *n.;* fear of, 25, 26, 27, 28, 36-37; knowledge and, 120-121; objectivity and, 115, 116, 140; reality of, 73-74, 111-112; of scientists, 50, 137, 138 *n.,* 139-140, 148; *see also specific emotions*
Empathy, 49-52, 96-97, 103, 112-114
Empiricism, 68-71; scientific, 135-137; values and, 146-147
*Encounter* (periodical), 90 *n.*
Endocrinology, *xv*
Esthetics, *xiv,* 31, 33; empathy in, 113; experience and, 75, 76; perception test, 62-64; rubricization and, 81-83; of science, 122, 123, 137, 148, 149, 150-151
Ethics, *xiv*
Ethnocentricity, scientific, *x,* 1
Ethnology, 116; empathy and, 113; idiographic questions in, 9-10; mechanistic view of, 4-6; observation in, 111; receptivity and, 97-98, 99
Ethology, 98, 99, 108
Euclid, 77, 80
Existentialism, *xvi,* 52, 120; abstraction and, 67-68
Experience, *xi;* contemplation and, 100; desacralization of, 139-144; of drug addiction, 58-61; education and, 60-64; esthetic, 81-83, 150-151; fusion, 103-104; 112-

114; knowledge and, 45-65, 74-75, 128, 133-134, 145; of love, 116-118; nature of, 148-149; "proof" of, 65; properties and characteristics of, 52-54; subjectivity and, 72-83; suchness of, 80, 81, 84-94; system and, 79-83; theory and, 77-79, 80
Experientialism, *xvi*
Experimental psychology, 12, 48; values of, 94 *n.*
Experiment, 13, 47, 95, 102; in value perception, 123-124
Explanation: desacralizing, 142; meaning and, 88, 89-90; and suchness-understanding, 92-94
Exploitation, 17

Family, 36, 37
Fascism, anti-intellectualism of, *xvi*
Fear: of control, 36, 37, 42, 107; of inflicting pain, 59, 139-140; of knowledge, 16-18, 20-32; knowledge of, 130; of love, 104, 140; neurosis and, 124-125; receptiveness and, 96; study of, 56; subjectivity of, 73; of uncertainty, 146; understanding and, 23 *n.*
Femininity, male attitudes toward, 27, 36-37, 38
*Form and Function: Remarks on Art* (Greenough), 150
Free association, 12, 54 *n.*
Freedom, 43; *see also* Spontaneity
Freud, Sigmund, 28; quoted, 11; on castration, 142; on defense mechanism, 22, 29; empiricism of, 77, 79; "free-floating attention," 98; methods of, *xiv,* 8, 104, 124; on primary process, 54
Friendship, *xix,* 140
Fromm, Erich, *xiv*
Fulfillment, 15
Fusion-knowledge, 52, 53, 103-104; experiential knowledge and, 112-114; I-Thou, 105

Gainsborough, Thomas, 82
Galileo Galilei, 9

Gamblers Anonymous, 46
Generalization: empirical, 68; motivation by fear, 27; particularity and, 8-11; theory and, 80
Geology, 9, 109
Gestalt psychology, 12
Goals. *See* Motivation
Gödel, 1
Goldstein, Kurt, 23; cited, 42, 69
Goodness, 15
Greenough, 150
Growth, *xiv,* 33-39, 71; knowledge and, 30-32; fear of, 28, 35-39; love and, 104; as motivation, 22, 23

Happiness: esthetic, 81-83; nature of, 148-149; of scientists, 92-94, 126, 137, 144; study of, 56; subjectivity of, 73
Hate, receptivity and, 115
Health, 14-15, 20, 30-32; meaning and, 87; self-knowledge and, 40-44, 48-49; values in, 144
Heisenberg, cited, 111
History: idiographic questions in, 9-10; interpersonal relationships in, 108; Newton's view of, 5 *n.*
Holism, *xiii-xiv, xv;* meaning and, 84; memory and, 66; methodology and, 8, 11-12; perception and, 62-64; 81-83; scientific values of, 143-144
Homosexuality, fear of, 37
Horney, Karen, *xiv,* 30 *n.,* 43
Humanistic tradition: emotion and, 112; empirical attitude and, 137; goals of, 40, 41; psychology and, 145 *n;* science and, 1-6, 120
Humor, 139, 144-148, 151
Hunger, cultural attitudes toward, 41
Huxley, Aldous, *xx*
Hysteria, 26, 35 *n.,* 63

Identification, knowledge and, 50-52
Identity, 55; emotions and, 73, 74; love and, 105; needs and, 124-125; *see also* Self-actualization

Idiographic knowledge, 8-11; *see also* Particularity
I-It knowledge: defined, 50; I-Thou knowledge contrasted, 105-107
Illusions, introspection and, 47
Imagination, 130 *n.*
Impulse: anti-intellectualism and, 63; desacralization and, 143; expression of, 41; identity and, 124-125
Impulsivity, *xvi;* fear and, 25, 26, 38-39; *see also* Spontaneity
Indians, 61 *n.* 6, 113
Individuality, *xiv; see also* Particularity; Personality
Individuation, 55; *see also* Identity; Self-actualization
Industry, 2
Insight, *xii,* 91, 104
Inspection concepts, 76 *n.*
Integration: dichotomizing versus, 34-35; of experiential and conceptual knowledge, 46-47, 49, 66-71, 86-94, 98-99, 101; of intuition and experience, 64; of objectivity and interpersonal relationships, 108-109; of objective and subjective approaches to knowledge, 54-58, 72-83; of scientific and human values, 149-151
Integrity, *x*
Intellectualization, 28-29
Interference. *See* Noninterference
Interpersonal relationships: analyst-patient, 10-11, 12, 13, 15, 17-18; experience and, 58-61; knowledge of, 102-118; projection in, 45 *n;* reality and, 74; *see also specific relationships, e.g.,* Friendship; Hate; Love
Introspection, 47, 105
Intuition, 76 *n.;* education and, 62-64; love and, 103; of meaning, 88-89; probability and, 132-133; scientific, 93, 129, 130
*Isaac Newton, Historian* (Manuel), 5 *n.*
I-Thou knowledge, 50-52, 102-118

James, William, quoted, 110 n.
Jews, 61 n. 6, 117
John Birch Society, 12, 113
John Dewey Society for the Study of Education and Culture, xii
Joy. See Happiness
Jung, Carl G., xiv, 124

Kierkegaard, Søren, 67
Knowledge: degree of, 128-137; emotion and, 111-112, 120-121; empirical, 146-147; experience and, 66-71, 81-83, 90, 145; fear of, 16-18, 20-32; I-Thou, 102-118; joy and, 137; modes of, 7-19, 45-65, 104-107; of motivation, 18-19; subjective, 73-74, 76; Taoist approach, 95-101; see also Philosophy; Science; Self-knowledge
Kubie, Lawrence, xiv
Kuhn, T. S., xx, 132; on "normal science," 2, 35

Laboratory psychology, 12
Language, 45 n.; communication and, 90-91; experience and, 46, 56 n.; limits of, 145; of psychoanalysis, 129-130; self-actualization and, 67
"Last Year at Marienbad" (Robbe-Grillet), 85 n.
Learning, 13, 68, 71, 110; defense mechanisms in, 26-30; holistic perception and, 62-64; see also Education; Knowledge
Leisure, xiv
Library (Apollodorus), 5 n.
Linguistic science, 108; see also Language
Linnaeus (Karl von Linné), 78
Listening, technique of, 96
Lobachevski, Nikolai I., 80
Logic, 4, 31; as defense mechanism, 24-26, 28; experience and, 54, 69, 91-92
Love, 15, 149, 151; contemplation and, 100, 147; cultural attitudes toward, 41; fear of, 36-37, 140; of knowledge, 16, 17-18, 20-32;

knowledge and, 51, 52, 103-104, 106-107; maturity and, 38; meaning, for the scientist, 109-110; neurosis and, 124-125; objectivity and, 116-118; orthodox methodology and, 47; in psychoanalysis, 17-18; receptivity and, 115; self-knowledge and, 41, 43; understanding and, 58-59, 60

Man, 2-3, 7; active and passive images of, 55; cognitive needs in, 20; "higher life" of, 13, 15, 121; meaning and, 84-85, 86; Newton's view of, 5 n; reality and, 111; see also Personality
Manas (periodical), xx
Manuel, Frank, xx; quoted, 5 n.
Masculinity, 26, 36-37, 38
Maslow, Abraham H., 119; quoted 3-4
Maslow Art Test, 62
Mathematics, 4, 63, 76; mechanistic tradition and, 9, 147; non-Euclidean, 77, 80; science and, 74, 102
Matson, Floyd, 2
Mauldin, Bill, 14
Maturity: factors in, x, xi; love and, 118; scientific, 35-39; sympathy and, 50; see also Growth
Meaning, 84-94
Mechanistic tradition, 1-6; abstraction and, 135; desacralization of science and, 137, 138-151; education and, 63-64; generalizing direction of, 9; limitations of knowledge in, 49-50; meaning and, 85-86, 91; methodology of, ix-xii, 7-11, 114; psychology and, 4-6, 102, 108, 147-148; values and, 15-16, 17, 44, 95
Medicine, 132, 133-134
Meeting of East and West, The (Northrop), xx
Memory, 66, 109, 110
Methodology: "analysis of the resistance," 16; behaviorism and, 13-16; interpersonal relationship

and, 12, 13, 102-118; mechanistic, *ix-xii,* 3-4, 114; motivation of, 29; objectivity and, 54-58; particularity and, 8-12; phenomenology and, 47; pluralism in, 56-57; Taoist, 95-101, 124; *see also specific methods, e.g.,* Conditioning

Motivation, 13, 18-19; deficiency, 22, 23, 24-26; growth, 22, 23; pathological, of cognitive needs, 26-30; of scientists, *xix,* 29-30, 92-94, 126-127, 145-146, 148-151

*Motivation and Personality* (Maslow), *xiii*

Murphy, William, quoted, 17 *n.*

Mysticism, 103-104

Nameche, G., cited, 116

National Society for College Teachers of Education, *xii*

Naziism, *xvi,* 120

Negroes, 61 *n.* 6, 117

Neurosis, 25-26, 29, 124-125

*Neurotic Personality of Our Time,* (Horney), 30 *n.*

Newton, Isaac, *xx,* 44, 146; political history and, 5 *n.*

Nietzsche, Friedrich, 67, 86

Nomothetic knowledge, 8-11; *see also* Generalization

Noninterference, 13, 53, 95; contemplative, 99-101; knowledge and, 10-11, 27, 96-99, 106; love and, 116

Norms, definition, 14-15

Northrop, F. C. S., *xx;* on intuition, 132; on language, 46; on reality, 76

Objectivity, 49-51, 70, 73, 75 *n.;* emotions and, 120-121, 140; psychiatry and, 102, 105-106; subjectivity and, 54-58; varieties of, 114-118

Objects: empathy with, 113; knowledge of, 49-52, 115, 145; memory span for, 66

Observation: knowledge and, 45-65; psychological, 54-58; reality and,

110-111; receptive, 96-97; self-knowledge and, 48-49

Order, 68-77, 100; contemplation and, 147; holistic perception and, 66-67; meaning and, 84, 87-88; pleasure in, 31; receptivity and, 98; security and, 24, 25-26, 30; simplification and, 74-75; theory and, 80-81

Orthodoxy, *ix-xii,* 1-6, 7, 49-50; addiction psychotherapy and, 60-61; creativeness and, 31-32, 33, 34; as defense, 33; and desacralization of science, 137; education and, 61 *n.* 7; empiricism and, 69-71; meaning and, 86; objectivity and, 55-58; problem-definition and, 14, 15-16; security and, 24; values and, 119-121

"Ought-perception," 59

Pain, helpful, 59

Paranoia, 26, 28, 121

Particularity: of experience, 84-94; generalization and, 8-11; modes of knowledge, 52

Passivity. *See* Receptivity

Patience. *See* Attentiveness; Receptivity

Peake, S. Joseph, cited, 138 *n.*

Perception: contemplation and, 99-101; holistic, 62-64, 66-67; love and, 110, 116; modes of knowledge and, 69-70, 81-83, 98-99, 106-107; objectivity and, 114-115; of reality, 98-99; of values, 123-124

Personality: fear and, 16-18, 23-26; healthy, 14-15; immature, 36-37; mature, 37-39; prediction and control of, 40-44; research methods and, *ix-xii, xiv,* 7-19, 52, 102-118; scientific, *xv-xvi,* 122-127, 128-137, 139-148, ethnocentricity, 1, honesty in, 48-49, humility in, 68, 71, integration of, 30-32, 34-39, isolation, 119, motivation, *xix,* 29-30, 92-94, 126-127, 145-146, 148-151, security needs, *ix, xiii,*

16-17, 22-23; self-knowledge and, 41; as subjectively active or passive, 54-58

*Personal Knowledge* (Polanyi), *xvi-xvii*

Pharmacology, 132

Phenomenology, 52; abstraction and, 67-68; experience and, 76; language and, 130

Philosophy, 1, 21, 121, 148; defensive, 23 *n.;* meaning and, 85-86; psychology and, *ix-xi, xix,* 3-4, 5, 7-8, 10, 55; self-actualization and, 67; self-control ideal of, 41

Physical sciences. *See specific sciences*

Physics, 102, 150; experience and, 76; mechanistic tradition and, 3, 9, 147; objectivity in, 114; observation in, 111; reality concept in, 100-101

Physiology, 150

Picasso, Pablo, quoted, 90 *n.*

Plato, 121

Polanyi, Michael, *xvi-xvii, xx;* on human motivation, 18; on scientific knowledge, 34 *n.;* on the scientific personality, 122, 132, 133

Politics, *xiv,* 2; interpersonal relationships in, 108

Portugal, 119

Positivism, objectivity of, 55-56

Postulation concepts, 76 *n.*

Preconscious, 19, 46, 99; experience and, 145; I-Thou knowledge and, 106

Predictability, 40, 42-44, 81

Prejudice, 17

Probability, certainty and, 131

Problems: of cognition, 22; definition of, 13-16, 129-131; doctrine and, 56-57; experiment and, 102; fear and, 23-26; pleasure in, 134-135; phenomenology and, 47

Projection, 25, 45 *n.,* 114-115

Protoknowledge, 133

Psychoanalysis, *xiv-xv;* empiricism and, 77, 79; friendship and, *xix;*

holistic approach in, 12; language of, 129-130; primary rule of, 54 *n.;* resistance to, 16-18

Psychodynamics, *xiv, xv, xix,* 8

*Psychologies of 1925* (Watson), 7

Psychology, 19, 108-110, 119-127; of Being, 91, 116; idiographic questions in, 9-10; mechanistic tradition and, 4-6, 102, 108, 147-148; observation in, 110-111; philosophy and, *ix-xi, xix,* 3-4, 5, 7-8, 10; professional status of, 145, 147-148; rehumanization of, 3-4, 7; research problems in, 135; of science (*See* Personality, scientific); values and, 121; *see also specific fields, e.g.,* Social psychology

Psychopathology, norms and, 14-15

Psychoses, 29

Psychosomatic medicine, *xv*

Psychotherapy, *x, xiv, xvi;* cognitive needs in, 22; experience and, 58-61; holistic approach in, 11; identity and, 124-125; interpersonal relationships and, 17-18, 104, 106-107; I-Thou knowledge in, 104-107; projection and, 45 *n.;* values in, 34

Race: ethnocentricity and, *x,* 1; objectivity and, 117; sympathy, 61 *n.* 6, 113

Rand, Harry, *xix*

Rank, *xiv*

Reality, *xi-xii,* 4, 123; acting out and, 19; classification and, 81-83; contemplation of, 99-101; defense mechanisms and, 47; emotion and, 111-112; empirical approach to, 68-69, 136; of experience, 79-80, 81, 86, 88-90; fear of, 23-26, 140-141; holistic perception and, 64; I-Thou knowledge and, 106-107; knowledge of, 146-147; meaning and, 85; mechanistic view of, 3; need to understand, 20-32; observation and, 110-111; limitations of perception, 66-67, 69-70, 72, 77-79, 80, 98-99; subjective, 73-74, 76-77

*Realms of Philosophy* (Sahakian and Sahakian), 121 *n.*

Real Self. *See* Identity.

Reason. *See* Logic

Receptivity, 10-11, 13, 27; biology and, 130 *n.*; control *versus*, 95-101; empirical, 68-71; esthetic, 62-64; experience and, 53, 54; I-Thou knowledge, 106; love and, 116; meaning and, 84; objectivity and, 115; understanding and, 72-73, 91-92

Reductiveness, *xiv, xv,* 4, 75; abstraction and, 69; desacralization and, 142-143; meaning and, 88; pleasure in, 93; psychology and, 11-12; theory and, 81; *see also* Abstraction

Reich, *xiv*

Religion, *xiv,* 2, 21, 23 *n.*; anti-intellectualism and, 63; immature views of, 37; orthodox, 33, 70-71, 119; science and, *xvi,* 86, 119, 137, 148, 151; self-control ideal of, 41; sympathy, 61 *n.* 6

*Religions, Values and Peak-Experiences* (Maslow), 119

"Remembering Eliot" (Spender), 90 *n.*

Renaissance, 120

Renoir, Pierre Auguste, 82

Reports, subjective, 12, 47

Repressions, 26, 47, 130

Resacralization. *See* Desacralization

Research, *ix-x, xii,* 4, 7-11; creativity and, 132-133, 134-137; empirical attitudes and, 135-137; in holistic perception, 62-64; on post-surgery visions, 142; problem definition in, 13-16; in value perception, 123-124

Resistance, in psychoanalysis, 16-18

Responsibility, 55, 122-123

Rilke, Rainer Maria, quoted, 14

Ritual, neurotic, 25, 26

Robbe-Grillet, Alain, 85 *n.*

Roe, Anne, *xx*

Rogers, C., 104

Rubricizing, 29, 62-63, 81-83; desacralizing tendency in, 143; in personal relations, 107

Russia, 70

Safety. *See* Security

Safety mechanisms. *See* Defense mechanisms

Sahakian, M., 121 *n.*

Sahakian, W., 121 *n.*

Saintliness, holistic perception and, 64

Sanctity. *See* Desacralization

Schizophrenia, 35 *n.*, 67, 73, 112

Science: anti-intellectualism and, 63; comprehensive and simpleward, 72-83; desacralization and resacralization of, 137, 138-151; empiricism and, 69-70; human values and, 2-4, 5, 7, 18-19, 149; impersonal model of, *xiii-xiv, xv-xvi,* 2, 8-11, 49-50, 54-58; institutionalization of, 119-121, 148; obligations of, *xi-xii,* 14, 33-34, 35, 72-76, 77-79, 82, 87-88, 101, 125-127, 134-135, 146-151; psychology of, 102-103, 108-110, 119-127 (*see also* Personality, scientific); *see also* specific disciplines; *and see* specific aspects of science, *e.g.,* Research

Security, *ix,* 1, 33-39; cognitive needs and, 20-23, 26-30; neurosis and, 124-125; order and, 24, 25-26, 30

Self-actualization, 55, 144; abstractness and, 67, 69; love and, 116; *see also* Growth; Maturity

Self-control: active, 54-55; obsession with, 38-39; self-knowledge and, 41, 43; self-respect and, 42

Self-knowledge: health and, 40-44; the scientist and, 48-49, 128

Self-respect, 41, 42, 55, 141

Semantics, 52; *see also* Communication

Sex, 17, 56 *n.*, 149; culture and, 41,

63; desacralization of, 141-142; identity, 27, 36, 37, 38
Simplicity, 93, 101; meaning and, 84, 88; scientific, 72-83, 88, 89
Social anthropology, 108
Social psychology, *xiv,* 17-18
Socialism, 70
Sociology, 108
Socrates, 142; on evil, 59
Solipsism, *xvi*
Sorokin, P., cited, 50
Spain, 119
Spectator knowledge, 49-52, 72; of drug addiction, 60-61; I-Thou knowledge contrasted with, 104-107
Spender, Stephen, cited, 90 *n.*
Spinoza, Baruch, 43
Spontaneity, 41, 55, 63-64
*Structure of Scientific Revolutions, The* (Kuhn), *xx*
*Study of Human Nature, The* (Watson), 111-112
Subjectivity, 54-58, 72-83, 136
Suchness, 80, 81; as meaning, 84-94
Surgery, 139, 140 *n.,* 142
Symbol, 19, 67, 77
Sympathy, 49-52, 96-97, 103, 112-114
Synanon, 46, 58-61
Systematizing, 77, 79-83, 121; of meaning, 87-88, 89

Taoism, *x, xvi,* 63, 104; methods of, 13, 95-101, 124
Taste, of the scientist, 122-123
Techniques. *See* Methodology
Technology, 61 *n.* 7, 73, 120; mechanistic tradition and, 3; science and, 135, 138, 139
Teratology, 9
Theory, 66-71, 98-99; limits of, 145, 146; obligations of, 77-79
Therapy. *See* Psychotherapy
Thoreau, Henry David, quoted, 146 *n.*
Tolman, Edward, 112
Torrance, E. P., on creativity, 38
Trainer, quoted, 61

Training, in research, *ix-x, xii; see also* Education
Transcendence, *xiv,* 15, 43, 48, 63; desacralization of science and, 121; objectivity and, 117; scientific, 144
Transference, 104, 130
Trust: experience and, 53, 60; in psychoanalysis, 17-18
Truth. *See* Reality

Unconscious, 19, 46, 99, 106, 145
Understanding, 43, 50-52, 76, 93; experience and, 58-61, 88-94; fear and, 23 *n.;* love and, 103, 107, 110; need for, 21, 26-30, 136; receptiveness and, 72-73; simplification and, 88, 89
Union of Soviet Socialist Republics, 70

Values: "antiscientific," *xv-xvi;* Being, 43, 141; desacralization of, 29, 139-144; esthetic, 62-64, 81-83; experience and, 53, 67, 91-92; human, 7, 15-16, 17, 44, 123, 124, 138, 139, 148-151; interpersonal relationship and, 12, 109-110, 116-117; mature, 37-38; mechanistic, 85-86, 91, 95, 114, 138, 139-140; need for, 21; nomothetic, 64; norm recognition, 14-15; objectivity and, 114-115; perception of, 59; psychology and, 10, 34; religious, 86; research and, *xii, xiv,* 1; scientific, 35, 72-75, 92-94, 119-129, 131, 136-138; systematic, 79-83; theoretical, 77-79, 80; Western, 41

Watson, David Lindsay, *xx;* quoted, 111-112
Watson, John, *x,* 7
West, The, *x,* 1-6, 41
Whitehead, Alfred North, quoted, 75
Whitman, Walt, quoted, 150 *n.*
Will, 55; experience and, 53, 54; meaning and, 85-86; of the scientist, 122-123; spectator-knowledge and, 106

Wilson, Colin, cited, 113
Wolff, Kurt, quoted, 96
Women: castration complex in, 141-142; happiness of, 148-149; receptivity of, 97
Wonder, varieties of, 148-151

*Writers At Work: Second Series (Viking Press),* 126 *n.*

Xanthippe, 142

Zen Buddhism, *xvi,* 52, 103